"Man Working," *1919–1962*

WILLIAM FAULKNER

A Catalogue of the William Faulkner

Collections at the University of Virginia

"Man Working," *1919–1962*

WILLIAM FAULKNER

A Catalogue of the William Faulkner Collections
at the University of Virginia

Compiled by Linton R. Massey

With an Introduction by John Cook Wyllie

Published by the Bibliographical Society of the University of Virginia
Distributed by the University Press of Virginia, Charlottesville

Copyright © 1968 by the Rector and Visitors
of the University of Virginia

The University Press of Virginia
First published 1968

Library of Congress Catalog Card: 68–19477
Printed in the United States of America

I. Three drafts of titles by Faulkner for the 1959 exhibition of his
works at the University of Virginia

FOREWORD

MAN WORKING was the title selected by William Faulkner to designate the comprehensive exhibition of his works at the University of Virginia Library in 1959, held to celebrate both the publication of *The Mansion* and the completion of his fortieth year as a professional man of letters.

"All right, but let this be the last show," he replied when his approval was sought, "and to make this the biggest of them all I'll send up a station wagon loaded with whatever Estelle can find in the attic at 'Rowan Oak.' I don't know what's left down there—working papers I never got around to burning, I guess, on *The Mansion*, *The Hamlet*, and some odds and ends left over from *A Fable*. But the point of your show at the University of Virginia ought to be the work a man can do after spending most of his lifetime at it, a man at work. That's not quite right; there ought to be some notion of continuity in the work." To a hesitant suggestion that "Genius Working" might be a more accurate substitute for the "Man Working" he finally came up with, Faulkner merely shook his head.

His final choice, good then, seems even better now as a means of indicating the magnitude of what he accomplished in the span of years from 1919 to 1962; and the idea of a "man working," as though Faulkner were still alive and would presently be found strolling down Rugby Road in Charlottesville, Virginia, with his usual air of imperturbability, appears to be beyond improvement in establishing once and for all "some notion of continuity" for the labors of a lifetime.

PREFACE

As THE catalogue of a collection devoted to a single American author this book makes no pretensions toward descriptive bibliography; it is not a check list, nor does it advance any claims to completeness. It does not even fully list the contents of the Faulkner Collections at the University because its terminal date for the inclusion of entries, fixed of necessity many months before publication, effectively prevented the addition of much newly acquired material in every category, in particular a substantial number of Faulkner letters and family papers. Despite these and other omissions, a great quantity of source materials is readily at hand for research scholars, with pointed emphasis on printed articles appearing during Faulkner's own lifetime.

Even a simple catalogue of so considerable a number of individual items imposed quite unforeseen problems. Some sections were arranged alphabetically as a matter of course, some chronologically as a matter of necessity. Attempts were made to cross-reference many of the entries, except in the case of printings of individual short stories, where the effort seemed unjustified; and, with each title page illustrated, descriptions of first editions were given only in part. Punctuation of publishers' names was regularized.

Brief descriptions of succeeding editions were given full titles, but a short form for publishers' names was used except in the case of those not very well known. Punctuation and capitalization of titles were standardized. In criticism the authors' own forms of reference to Faulkner's works were adopted, again with uniform titles. In citations the name of the author was usually given, followed by the title of the article, name of journal, place of publication if required, volume, date, and page. In some instances where reproduced material had been substituted for originals, not all the information was available. A standard form of title was chosen for journals having slightly altered names over the period of their publication.

The complete transcription of the title page of the major books lies in the facsimile only. Further details of the collation of these volumes follow a catchword identification of the title page, which is intended to identify the facsimile and is in no sense itself a transcript. Because the title page facsimiles vary widely in reduction ratios, the actual height of the page is given in the collation.

As a whole the finished catalogue is actually the work of many collaborators, in that once the original compilation had been made, each entry was verified by four dedicated experts, each intent upon accuracy and each resolved not to introduce errors of his own. Mr. Matthew J. Bruccoli, now Professor of English at Ohio State University, performed valiant service; he was succeeded by Mrs. Stuyvesant K. Bearns, who brought diligence and industry to a tedious task. Mr. William S. Kable, now on the staff of the English Department of the University of South Carolina, meticulously edited the text and made substantial contributions of his own. As final arbiter, Mr. Jeffrey Gross, of the English Department, University of Virginia, gave help of incalculable value; his services proved to be indispensable.

Mr. John Cook Wyllie, Director of Libraries of the University of Virginia, advised, consoled, and, above all, encouraged during those forbidding moments when enthusiasm for the job in hand dwindled to the point where it became indistinguishable from apathy. All the friends, correspondents, and dealers who indirectly contributed to the genesis of the present volume are due these thanks, however belated; and to Mrs. Louis Henry Cohn, who over the years supplied much of the printed material, must come this most inadequate accolade.

Perfunctory thanks would be equally amiss in acknowledging with profound gratitude the indulgence, graciousness, and confidence bestowed upon this venture by Mrs. William Faulkner and Mrs. Jill Faulkner Summers, who gave without the slightest demur their blessings and a carte blanche to reproduce without any restrictions whatever such holograph or typescript material as might be deemed suitable to illustrate and enliven these pages.

Their heart-warming faith imposed solemn responsibilities that could never, *Deo volente*, be abused, and could only be repaid with unfaltering loyalty and affection.

But despite all the collective talents here mustered, paraded, and saluted; for all the slavery and drudgery and energy expended; for all the care exercised and the vigilance bestowed, there will be errors—fivefold, no less!—as some ungenerous soul might gleefully assert.

For these unforgivable sins of no matter what degree, the compiler assumes entire responsibility with no hesitation whatever, if only as a penance, and if only out of respect for those disciplines this hitherto unrecorded labor of Hercules obliged him to cultivate.

L. R. M.

Keswick, Virginia, April 1967

CONTENTS

PLATES

INTRODUCTION

In scope, magnitude, and depth, the Faulkner Collections described in these pages can hardly be equaled elsewhere; altogether they constitute one of the largest and most important assemblages of works by and relating to any single modern author.

While Writer-in-Residence at the University, William Faulkner became aware of the Massey collection of his works, and despite his native diffidence and pretended unconcern, this awareness undoubtedly contributed to his wish, reaffirmed by his wife and daughter, to have his manuscripts and typescripts made available at the University of Virginia, where they might serve to supplement and complement a rather more than adequate representation of his life's work.

Mr. Massey, who claims to be not really a collector, was induced by the brilliant techniques of *As I Lay Dying* to go back to earlier published books, thence forward as the author's career advanced, picking up here and there a treasure or two no one then seemed to want, such as a twice-inscribed copy of *The Marble Faun* for $12.50, or a series of holograph letters at $5.00 each. Gradually over the years his acquisitions grew until they overflowed all available shelf space and compelled him to seek relief in utilizing the more ample facilities of the Alderman Library.

His collection of unique copies of the printed books, of letters, poems, manuscripts and typescripts, documents, and private papers, speaks for itself. His attention to depth, with multiple copies and successive editions to facilitate study and collation, is notable. Foreign editions add a savor of their own. Critical materials form an extensive division of considerable convenience to research students.

Standing beside all these, on extended deposit by the William Faulkner Foundation, are the surviving Faulkner manuscripts and typescripts, many with trial versions heavy with authorial corrections and proof states showing additional revisions. These, too, speak most eloquently for themselves. Through Faulkner's foresight and by the unselfish agreement of his heirs, these papers of inestimable value to students of Faulkner's books remain in Virginia.

They are a monument to the author's warm and responsive attachment to an institution that had adopted him out of respect and admiration for his genius.

John Cook Wyllie

Alderman Library
University of Virginia
April 1967

Part One: Works by Faulkner

THE novels are arranged alphabetically. American and foreign editions in English (usually British) are followed by translations. Proof, when it occurs, precedes the relevant editions. Reprints follow editions from which they are taken. Excerpts, references to published reproductions of manuscript and typescript pages, and other related material follow other entries from the same country of origin. The annotations about bindings follow Blanck.

ABSALOM, ABSALOM!

1 *Absalom, Absalom!*
New York: Random House, 1936.
The title is in red; the rest of the title page is printed in black.
[1–24⁸], 192 ll., 2 inserts.
pp. [1–6] 7–384.   26 cm.
Laid paper, watermarked "Holliston Text." Front and back covered with printed paper, green V-cloth shelfback; spine gold-stamped.   Top edge gold.
Certificate of limitation: ". . . limited to 300 copies, signed by the author, of which this is number [ ]," tipped in facing p. [4].
Fold-out map of Jefferson tipped in facing p. 384.
The trade and limited copies of this book are from the same printing.
Copy 1: Number 224, inscribed, "To Bill Conselman Bill Faulkner Studio 19 November 1936." Copy 2: Number 44.
First edition, first printing.

2 ——. New York: Random House, [1936].
Same title page as limited printing.
[1–24⁸], 192 ll., 1 insert.
pp. [1–6] 7–384.
Unwatermarked laid paper.   Black V-cloth; front, back, and spine stamped in red and gold.   Top edge red.
Fold-out map of Jefferson tipped in facing p. 384.
Copy 1 and copy 2: Printed dust jacket.   Copy 3.
First edition, first printing.

William Faulkner

Absalom, Absalom!

New York · Random House · 1936

Title page of No. 1

3 ——.   New York: Modern   Library,   1951.
Introduction by Harvey Breit.   First edition, "First Modern Library Edition 1951."   Two copies.

American Excerpts

4 "Absalom, Absalom!" *American Mercury*, XXXVIII, No. 152 (August 1936). Working version of first chapter of the novel.

"Wedding in the Rain." See 494 *The Portable Faulkner*, ed. Malcolm Cowley, 1946, and related entries.

5 "Two and Two Makes Five." *The World from Jackson Square*, ed. Etolia S. Basso. New York: Farrar, Straus, 1948.

Illustrations of MSS, Typescripts, Etc.

6 Reproduction of first MS page. *Benefit Auction . . . under the Auspices of The League of American Writers . . . for the Benefit of Exiled Writers . . . January 14th, 1940.* N.p., n.d.

7 ——. Bertram Rota. "Contemporary Collectors VII—The George Lazarus Library," *Book Collector*, IV (Winter 1955).

Reproduction of pp. 9 and 13 of the revised typescript. See 2768 Meriwether, James B., "The Literary Career of William Faulkner," *Princeton University Library Chronicle*, XXI, No. 3 (Spring 1960) and 2766 his *The Literary Career of William Faulkner*, 1961.*

BRITISH EDITIONS

8 *Absalom, Absalom!*
London: Chatto & Windus, [ca. 1936].
Same collation and pagination as first American trade printing.
Laid paper. Buff V-cloth; front and spine stamped in red and black.
The American sheets, the title page conjugate and bearing the Chatto & Windus imprint.
First edition, first British publication.

9 ——. London: Chatto & Windus, 1960. First edition, reprint.

* Hereafter these two works will be cited as Meriwether, "Career," and Meriwether, *Career*, respectively.

TRANSLATIONS

French

10 *Absalon! Absalon!* Paris: Gallimard, 1953. Trans. R.-N. Raimbault and Ch.-P. Vorce. Copy 1: Trade edition. Copy 2: Number 68 of 80 on "vélin pur fil Navarre."

Excerpts

"Le mariage de Sutpen." See 1006 *Jefferson, Mississippi*, 1956. Trans. R.-N. Raimbault.

German

11 *Absalom, Absalom!* Hamburg: Rowohlt, 1956. Trans. Hermann Stresau. "9–12 Tausend."

Italian

12 *Assalonne, Assalonne!* Milan: Mondadori, 1954. Trans. with preface by Glauco Cambon. "Iª edizione."

See 1007 *Tutte le opere di William Faulkner*, Vol. III–IV, 1961. The Cambon translation.

Spanish

13 *¡Absalón, Absalón!* Buenos Aires: Emecé, 1951. Trans. Beatriz Florencia Nelson. "Segunda edición."

14 ——. 1958. "Cuarta impresión."

See 1009 *Obras escogidas*, Vol. II, 1962. Trans. Amando Lazaro Ros.

Miscellaneous

See 1011 *Gendai Amerika bungaku zenshu*, Vol. VIII, 1958.

15 *Absalomie, Absalomie . . .* Warsaw: Państwowy Instytut Wydawniczy, 1959. Trans. with afterword by Zofia Kierszys.

16 *As I Lay Dying*
New York: Jonathan Cape and Harrison Smith, [1930].
   [1–15⁸ 16¹⁰], 130 ll.
   pp. [i–vi] 1–254. 19 cm.
   Beige V-cloth; front and spine brown-stamped. Beige endpapers.
   On copyright page: "First Published, 1930."
   Three copies in printed dust jacket. Copy 1: First state, with the dropped "I" on p. 11 and top edge stained dark brown. Copy 2: Second state, with the "I" correctly positioned and top edge stained light brown; signed on the title page, "William Faulkner Los Angeles Cal 25 May 1932." Copy 3: Second state, as in copy 2, but this copy only has the damaged serif in "I" on the front cover. Copy 4: Second state.
   First edition, first printing.

17 The Sound and the Fury *&* As I Lay Dying. New York: Modern Library (Random House), 1946. With slightly revised appendix to the Viking *Portable Faulkner* here used as the foreword. A new setting of both novels. First joint edition, presumably first printing. Two copies.

18 ———. [ca. 1954]. First joint edition, reprint. Paperback.

19 *As I Lay Dying.* New York: Vintage Books (Random House), 1964. Revised edition, reset; "First Vintage Edition, March, 1964." Paperback.

American Excerpts

See 1013 *Faulkner Reads from His Works*, Caedmon, TC 1035 (1954).

Illustrations of MSS, Typescripts, Etc.

Reproduction of first MS page. See 893 Stein and related entries.

AS I LAY DYING

WILLIAM FAULKNER

NEW YORK

JONATHAN CAPE: HARRISON SMITH

Title page of No. 16

Reproduction of last MS page. See 2769 Meriwether, James B., "William Faulkner: A Check List," * and 2766 his *Career.*

* Hereafter this work will be referred to as Meriwether, "Check List."

BRITISH EDITIONS

20   *As I Lay Dying*
London: Chatto & Windus, 1935.
[A]⁴ B–Q⁸ R⁴, 128 ll., 2 inserts.
pp. [i–viii] 1–248.
Laid paper. Blue V-cloth; spine white-stamped. Top edge blue. Printed dust jacket.
Two leaves of advertisements inserted following p. 248.
First British edition, first printing.

21 ——. London: Chatto & Windus, 1958. First British edition, reprint.

——. See 445 *Faulkner's County*, 1955.

22 ——. Harmondsworth: Penguin Books, 1963. Penguin Modern Classics. Paperback.

TRANSLATIONS

French

23   *Tandis que j'agonise*. Paris: Gallimard, 1934. Trans. Maurice-E. Coindreau. Preface by Valery Larbaud. Copy 1: Number 6 of 150 on "alfa Lafuma-Navarre." Copy 2: Number 10 of 60 "hors commerce" on the same paper.

24 ——. Paris: Boisseau, 1946. The Coindreau translation. Unsewn gatherings, boxed. Copy 1: Number 18 of 25 on "auvergne à la main avec suite de toutes les gravures." Copy 2: Number 49 of 175 on "pur fil de lana."

Excerpts

25   "Dewey Dell." *Études américaines*, Cahier X (1948), 22–23. Translator not given.

German

26   *Als ich im Sterben lag*. Zurich: Fretz & Wasmuth, 1961. Trans. Albert Hess and Peter Schünemann.

27 ——. Stuttgart: Goverts, 1961. The Hess and Schünemann translation.

Italian

28   *Mentre morivo*. Milan: Mondadori, 1958. Trans. Giulio de Angelis. "1 Edizione."

Spanish

29   *Mientras yo agonizo*. Buenos Aires: Rueda, 1952. Trans. with preface by Max Dickmann. Four copies.

30   *Mientras agonizo*. Madrid: Aguilar, 1954. Trans. Agustín Caballero Robredo and Arturo del Hoyo. Introduction not signed.

See 1009 *Obras escogidas*, Vol. I, 1956, and 1008 *Obras completas*, Vol. II, 1962. The Caballero Robredo and del Hoyo translation in both.

Miscellaneous

31   *Kun tein kuolemaa*. Helsinki: Kustannusosakeyhtiö Tammi, 1952. Trans. with preface by Alex. Matson.

32   *I min sidste time*. Copenhagen: Andersen, [1954]. Trans. Gunnar Juel Jørgensen.

33   *Uitvaart in Mississippi*. Amsterdam: Bezige Bij, 1955. Trans. Apie Prins and John Vandenbergh. "Eerste druk."

See 1012 *Shino tokoni yo kotawannte*, 1959. Trans. Masami Nishikawa.

34   *Na minha morte*. Lisbon: Edição "Livros do Brasil," [1964]. Trans. Alfredo Margarido.

Excerpts

35   "Addie." *All världens berättare* (Stockholm), V (May 1946). Trans. Jöran Mjöberg.

36 *A Fable*. Galley proof. Galleys 1–310. Blue covers, printed in black.

37 *A Fable*
New York: Random House, [1954].
The second cross on the title page is blue; the rest is printed in black.
[1–14¹⁶,] 224 ll., 1 insert.
pp. [i–x] [1–3] 4–437 [438]. 21.3 cm.
Blue V-cloth; blue and white crosses stamped on front, spine stamped in gold and white. Top edge blue. Blue-gray endpapers. Boxed.
Certificate of limitation: ". . . limited to one thousand copies, signed by the author. Number [409]," tipped in before p. [1].
On copyright page: "First Printing."
The trade and limited copies are from the same printing.
First edition, first printing.

38 ——. New York: Random House, [1954].
Title page printed all in black.
[1–14¹⁶], 224 ll.
pp. [i–x] [1–3] 4–437 [438].
Maroon V-cloth; blue and maroon crosses stamped on front, spine stamped in silver and tan. Top edge blue-gray. Blue-gray endpapers. Printed dust jacket.
On copyright page: "First Printing."
First edition, first printing.

39 ——. New York: Random House, [1954]. First edition, "Second Printing."

40 ——. [1954]. First edition, "Third Printing."

41 ——. [ca. 1954]. First edition, reprint.

Title page of No. 37

Illustrations of MSS, Typescripts, Etc.

42 Seven photographs on 9½″ x 11½″ mounts of the plot of *A Fable* from the wall at "Rowan Oak." Reproduced in *Life* magazine; see next entry.

43 "Faulkner Wall Plot." *Life*, XXXVII, No. 6 (August 9, 1954). Photographs show outlines of *A Fable* made on the wall of Faulkner's study.

American Excerpts

See 1013 *Faulkner Reads from His Works*, Caedmon, TC 1035 (1954).

44 "William Faulkner." *A Great Books Reader II.* Chicago: Great Books Foundation, 1957.

BRITISH EDITIONS

45 *A Fable.* Proof copy. London: Chatto & Windus, 1955. Gray wrappers, printed in black.

46 *A Fable*
London: Chatto & Windus, 1955.
A–M¹⁶ N⁴, 196 ll.
pp. [1–8] 9–391 [392].
Red V-cloth; spine gold-stamped. Printed dust jacket.
First British edition, first printing.

TRANSLATIONS

French

47 *Parabole.* Paris: Gallimard, 1958. Trans. R.-N. Raimbault. Number 20 of 76 on "vélin pur fil Lafuma-Navarre."

German

48 *Eine Legende.* Zurich: Fretz & Wasmuth, 1955. Trans. Kurt Heinrich Hansen.

49 ——. Stuttgart: Scherz & Goverts, 1955. The Hansen translation published simultaneously in Zurich.

Spanish

50 *Una fábula.* Barcelona: Éxito, 1955. Trans. Antonio Ribera. Introduction by Agustín Bartra.

51 ——. Buenos Aires: Editorial Jackson de Ediciones Selectas, 1956. The Ribera translation with introduction by Bartra.

See 1008 *Obras completas*, Vol. II, 1962. The Ribera translation.

See 1009 *Obras escogidas*, Vol. II, 1962. Trans. Amando Lazaro Ros.

Miscellaneous

52 *Uma fábula.* São Paulo–Rio de Janeiro: Merito, 1956. Trans. with preface by Olivia Krähenbühl.

53 *Guwa.* Tokyo: Iwanami, 1960. Trans. Tomoji Abe. First edition; two copies.

54 *Baj.* Prague: Stáiní Nakladatelstyí Krásné Literatury a Umění, 1961. Trans. Josef Škvorecký and Lubomír Dorůžka. Two copies.

GO DOWN, MOSES

See 448–462. Faulkner himself, and many of his critics, believed this book, like *The Unvanquished*, to be a novel. The inconsistency in the present listing is not a judgment on this point, but rather has been introduced because of the nature of the publication history.

55 *The Hamlet*
New York: Random House, 1940.
The title page illustration is in blue, white, rose, yellow, and green; the type is in blue.
[1–27⁸], 216 ll., 2 inserts.
pp. [i–viii] [1–2] 3–421 [422–424]. 20.5 cm.
Green V-cloth, front and back covered with pale-green paper; spine gold-stamped. Top edge gold.
Certificate of limitation: ". . . limited to 250 copies and signed by the author. Number [161]," tipped in facing p. [ii].
Pictorial title page tipped in facing p. [iv].
On copyright page: "First Printing."
The trade and limited copies are from the same printing.
First edition, first printing.

56 ——. New York: Random House, 1940.
Same title page as limited printing.
[1–27⁸], 216 ll., 1 insert.
pp. [i–viii] [1–2] 3–421 [422–424].
Black V-cloth; front and spine stamped in red and gold. Top edge red. Printed dust jacket.
Pictorial title page tipped in facing p. [iv].
On copyright page: "First Printing."
First edition, first printing.

57 ——. New York: Random House, 1940. First edition, "Second Printing."

58 ——. [1956]. Second American edition, probably reprint.

59 ——. [1956]. Second American edition, probably reprint. Modern Library Paperback.

60 ——. [1964]. "Third Edition 1964," first printing as part of the Snopes Trilogy.

Title page of No. 55

American Excerpts

"Spotted Horses." See 494 *The Portable Faulkner*, ed. Malcolm Cowley, 1946, and related entries; 443 *The Faulkner Reader*, 1954, and related entries; 515 *Three*

Famous Novels, 1958; and 684, 685, and 686 under single short stories.

61   *The Long Hot Summer*.   New York: New American Library, 1958.   Third American edition, "First printing."   Two copies.

"From *The Hamlet*."   See 544 *Bear, Man, and God*, ed. Francis Lee Utley *et al.*, 1964.

Illustrations of MSS, Typescripts, Etc.

Reproduction of MS p. 2 of "Father Abraham" and typescript p. 18 of "Abraham's Children."   (Both are partial early versions of *The Hamlet*.)   See 2768 and 2766 Meriwether, "Career" and *Career*.

Reproduction of first MS page.   See 2769 and 2766 Meriwether, "Check List" and *Career*.

BRITISH EDITIONS

62   *The Hamlet*
     London: Chatto & Windus, 1940.
     [A]⁴ B–Y⁸, 172 ll.
     pp. [i–vi] vii [viii] [1–2] 3–333 [334–336].
     Laid paper.   Yellow V-cloth; spine stamped in blue-green.   Top edge yellow.   Printed dust jacket.
     First British edition, first printing.

British Excerpts

"Spotted Horses."   See 445 *Faulkner's County*, 1955.

TRANSLATIONS

French

63   *Le hameau*.   Paris: Gallimard, 1959.   Trans. René Hilleret.   Number 37 of 66 on "vélin pur fil Lafuma-Navarre."

German

64   *Das Dorf*.   Stuttgart: Goverts, 1957.   Trans. Helmut M. Braem and Elisabeth Kaiser.

Italian

65   *Il borgo*.   Milan: Mondadori, 1943.   Trans. Cesare Pavese.   "2ª edizione."

66   ——.   1958.   "IV edizione."

Spanish

67   *El villorrio*.   Barcelona: Caralt, 1953.   Trans. J. Napoletano Torre and P. Carbó Amiguet.   "Primera edición."

See 1009 *Obras escogidas*, Vol. I, 1956, and 1008 *Obras completas*, Vol. I, 1959.   The Napoletano Torre and Carbó Amiguet translation in both.

68   *El villorrio*.   Buenos Aires: Libros del Mirasol, 1961.   Trans. Santos Merino.   Three copies.

Miscellaneous

69   *Zascianek*.   Warsaw: Czytelnik, 1964.   Trans. Kalina Wojciechowska.

70   *A aldeia*.   Lisbon: Editora Arcádia, [1965].   Trans. Jorge Sampaio.

71 *Intruder in the Dust.* Galley proof. Galleys 4–81A. Stapled in blue paper covers; printed label on front.

72 *Intruder in the Dust*
New York: Random House, [1948].
The initial "I" and "D" are in blue; the rest of the title page is printed in black.
[1–8¹⁶], 128 ll.
pp. [i–vi] [1–2] 3–247 [248–250]. 20.3 cm.
Black V-cloth; front and spine stamped in blue and gold. Top edge blue. Printed dust jacket.
On copyright page: "First Printing."
First edition, first printing.

73 ——. New York: Random House, [ca. 1948]. First edition, "second printing." Two copies.

74 ——. [ca. 1948]. First edition, "third printing."

75 ——. [ca. 1948]. First edition, "sixth printing."

76 ——. [ca. 1948]. First edition, "eighth printing."

77 ——. New York: New American Library, 1949. Second American edition, "second printing."

78 ——. 1958. Third American edition, probably reprint, "seventh printing."

79 ——. 1960. Third American edition, reprint, "eighth printing."

80 ——. New York: Modern Library, [1964]. Reprint.

American Excerpts

81 *Intruder in the Dust. Omnibook*, XI, No. 1 (December 1948). An abridgment.

Intruder
in the
Dust

by

William Faulkner

Random House
New York

Title page of No. 72

82 "Jefferson, Mississippi." *Prose for Comparison*, ed. Eleanor Terry Lincoln. New York: Norton, 1956. With *A Manual for Instructors*.

Illustrations of MSS, Typescripts, Etc.

Reproduction of p. 65 of the revised typescript. See 2769 and 2766 Meriwether, "Check List" and *Career*.

BRITISH EDITIONS

83   *Intruder in the Dust*
     London: Chatto & Windus, 1949.
     [A]⁸ B–P⁸ Q⁶, 126 ll.
     pp. [i–iv] [1–2] 3–247 [248].
     Blue V-cloth; spine gold-stamped.   Top edge blue-green.   Printed dust jacket.
     Copy 1 and copy 2.
     First edition, first British reprint.

84   ——. London: Chatto & Windus, 1957.   First edition, reprint.

85   ——. Harmondsworth: Penguin, 1960.   First British edition, first printing.

TRANSLATIONS

French

86   *L'intrus.* Paris: Gallimard, 1952.   Trans. R.-N. Raimbault.   Copy 1: Number 106 of 131 on "vélin pur fil des Papeteries Lafuma-Navarre."   Copy 2: Number 1,167, "exemplaire sur alfa h. c."

German

87   *Griff in den Staub.* Stuttgart–Hamburg: Scherz & Goverts, 1951.   Trans. Harry Kahn.

88   ——. Darmstadt: Bürgers Taschenbücher, n.d. The Kahn translation.

Italian

89   *Non si fruga nella polvere.* Milan: Mondadori, 1951.   Trans. with introduction by Fernanda Pivano. "I edizione."

See 1007 *Tutte le opere di William Faulkner*, Vol. II, 1960.   The Pivano translation.

Spanish

90   *Intruso en el polvo.* Buenos Aires: Losada, 1951. Trans. Aída Aisenson.

91   ——. 1959.   "Segunda Edición."

Miscellaneous

92   *Inkräktare i stoftet.* Stockholm: Bonniers, 1950. Trans. Th. Warburton.

93   *Ubuden gaest i støvet.* Copenhagen: Aschehoug, 1950.   Trans. Moges Boisen.

94   *Ongenode Gast.* Amsterdam–Antwerp: Wereld-Bibliotheek, 1951.   Trans. Apie Prins.

95   *Hakaba e no chinny-sha.* Tokyo: Hayakawa Shobō, 1953.   Trans. Shōzō Kajima.

96   *Uljez u prašinu.* Belgrade: Novo prokoljenje, 1953.   Trans. into Serbian by Svetozar Brkić.

97   *O mundo não perdoa.* Lisbon: Publicações Europa–America, 1954.   Trans. António de Sousa. "Segunda edição"; two copies.

98   *Neodpočívej v pokoji.* Prague: Naše Vojsko, 1958.   Trans. Jiří Valja.   Afterword by Dr. Libuše Bubeníková.   Two copies.

99   *Intruz.* Warsaw: Czytelnik, 1961.   Trans. Ewa Życieńska.

100 *Uljez u prašinu.* Sarajevo: Svetjetlost, 1963. Trans. into Croatian by Svetozar Brkić.

101 *Sírgyalázók.* Budapest: Magvetö, 1964.   Trans. into Hungarian by György Déri.

102 ——. New York: Harrison Smith and Robert Haas, [1932]. Salesman's dummy. [1 (13 leaves). pp. [1–26]. Green V-cloth; blind-stamped on front and green-stamped on spine. A blank gathering of eight leaves with sample title page tipped in following leaf one and sample pages numbered 1 and 2 tipped in after leaves two and three respectively. These two pages of text differ markedly from the published novel.

103 *Light in August*
New York: Harrison Smith and Robert Haas, [1932].
[1–15^{16} 16^2], 242 ll.
pp. [i–iv] 1–480. 20.3 cm.
Coarse-grained tan V-cloth; front stamped in orange and spine stamped in orange and blue. Top edge orange.
On copyright page: "First Printing."
The mistake at 340.1 of "Jefferson" for "Mottstown" appears in all Smith & Haas printings and is repeated in the New Directions and Chatto & Windus reprints.
Four copies in printed dust jacket. Copy 1: Inscribed on the free front endpaper, "For Richard Weil William Faulkner Studio. 19 March 1944," and signed "William Faulkner" on the title page. Copy 2, copy 3, and copy 4.
First edition, first printing.

104 ——. 1932. First edition, "second printing."

105 ——. 1932. First edition, "third printing." Two copies.

106 ——. 1932. First edition, "fourth printing."

107 ——. Norfolk: New Directions, [ca. 1947]. First edition, reprint. Two copies.

108 ——. New York: Modern Library, [ca. 1950]. Introduction by Richard H. Rovere. 314.8 reads "Jefferson." Second edition, presumably first printing.

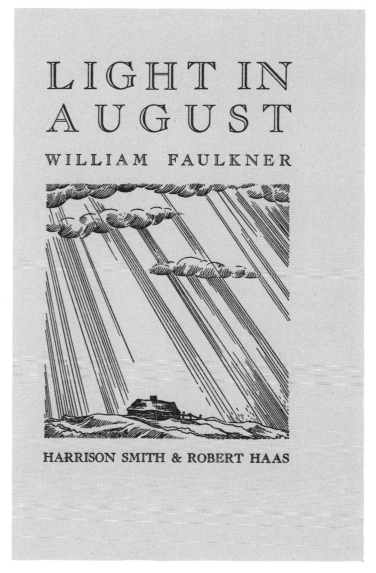

Title page of No. 103

American Excerpts and Related Items

"Percy Grimm." See 494 *The Portable Faulkner*, ed. Malcolm Cowley, 1946, and related entries; also 443 *The Faulkner Reader*, 1954, and related entries.

109 "Hitchhikers." *Great Scenes from Great Novels,* ed. Robert Terrall. New York: Dell, 1956. "First printing."

See 1015 *Faulkner Reads from His Works.* Phonodisc: M–G–M, E 3617 ARC (1957).

Illustrations of MSS, Typescripts, Etc.

Reproduction of MS page from an early draft. See 2790 Texas, *William Faulkner: An Exhibition of Manuscripts,* 1959.

BRITISH EDITIONS

110 *Light in August*
     London: Chatto & Windus, 1933.
     [A]⁸ B–Z⁸ AA–FF⁸ GG¹⁰, 242 ll.
     pp. [i–iv] 1–480.
     Red V-cloth; spine gold-stamped. Top edge red. Printed dust jacket.
     First edition, first British printing.

111 ——. London: Chatto & Windus, 1952. First edition, reprint.

112 ——. Harmondsworth: Penguin, 1960. Third edition, first printing.

British Excerpts

"Percy Grimm." See 445 *Faulkner's County,* 1955.

TRANSLATIONS

French

113 *Lumière d'août.* Paris: Gallimard, 1935. Trans. with introduction by Maurice-E. Coindreau. Number 11 of 20 copies "hors commerce sur Alfa Navarre."

114 ——. 1948. Reprint of 1935 edition. Number 264 of 990 copies on "alfa des Papeteries Navarre."

115 ——. Paris: Le Livre de Poche, [1961]. The Coindreau translation and introduction.

116 ——. Paris: Gallimard, [1964]. The Coindreau translation. Collection Soleil, Number 1042 of 3100 copies.

German

117 *Licht im August.* Berlin: Rowohlt, 1935. Trans. Franz Fein. "1–3 Tausend."

118 ——. Hamburg: Rowohlt, 1955. New edition of the Fein translation. Two copies.

119 ——. Munich–Zurich: Knaur, [1962]. New edition of the 1935 translation.

Italian

120 *Luce d'agosto.* Milan: Mondadori, 1939. Trans. Elio Vittorini. "Iᵃ Edizione."

121 ——. 1954. New edition of the Vittorini translation. "Iᵃ Edizione."

Spanish

122 *Luz de agosto.* Buenos Aires: Sur, 1942. Trans. Pedro Lecuona.

123 ——. Buenos Aires: Goyanarte, 1957. The Lecuona translation.

Miscellaneous

124 *Mørk august.* Oslo: Gyldendal, 1934. Trans. Sigurd Hoel.

125 ——. 1951. New edition of the Hoel translation.

126 *Luz de agôsto.* Rio de Janeiro–Porto Allegre–São Paulo: Globo, 1948. Trans. Berenice Xavier.

127 *Ljus i augusti.* Stockholm: Bonniers, 1950. Trans. Eril Lindegren. "Femte sjätte tusendet."

128 *Geboorte in Augustus.* Amsterdam: Querido, 1951. Trans. I. E. Prins-Willekes Macdonald. "Tweede Druke."

129 *Svijetlo u Augustu.* Zagreb: Zora, 1953. Trans. into Croatian by Šime Balen.

130 *Światłość w Siernpniu.* Warsaw: Czytelnik, 1959. Trans. Maciej Słomczynski.

131 *Hachigatsu no hikari.* Tokyo: Kawade Shobō, 1961. Trans. Masaō Takahashi. First edition.

132 *Megszületik augusztusban.* Budapest: Európa Könyvkiadó, 1961. Trans. into Hungarian by György Déri. Appendix by Mihály Sükosd.

133 ———. 1964. The Hungarian translation by Déri, with appendix by Sükosd.

134 *Forløsning i august.* Oslo: Gyldenhal, 1964. Trans. Sven Møller Kristensen.

135 *Llum d'agost.* Barcelona: El Balancí, [1965]. Trans. into Catalan by Manuel de Pedrolo.

Excerpts

See 503 *Sem' rasskazov*, 1958.

136 "Svet v avguste." *Amerika.* Washington: United States Information Agency, 1963. In addition to an excerpt from *Light in August* in Russian, this has a cover photograph of William Faulkner in color and an informative article about him.

137 *The Mansion.* Galley proof. Galleys 1–153.

138 ——. Temporarily paged galley proof. II–V, VII, VI, VIII–X, 1–305/306 p. Blue covers printed in black, spiral binding, the pages made up from half-galleys Nos. 1–153 with prelims added. The blue cover carries the title: Uncorrected Proof from / Random House / [Rule] / The Mansion / by William Faulkner / [Rule]

The pagination in this proof does not correspond with the pagination in the printed book.

139 *The Mansion*

New York: Random House, [1959].

The author's name in blue, the rest of the title page printed in black.

[1–14^{16}], 224 ll., 1 insert.

pp. [i–xii] [1–2] 3–436. 20.4 cm.

Laid paper. Black V-cloth; front and spine gold-stamped. Top edge blue. Blue endpapers.

Certificate of limitation ". . . limited to five hundred copies, signed by the author. Number [75]," tipped in before p. [i].

On copyright page: "First Printing."

The limited and trade copies are from the same printing.

First edition, first printing.

140 ——. New York: Random House, [1959]. "Limited, signed, edition," but this copy is an out-of-series book, with a certificate of limitation bearing no number and no signature.

141 ——. Same title page as the limited copy.

[1–14^{16}], 224 ll.

pp. [i–xii] [1–2] 3–436.

Laid paper. Blue V-cloth; front and spine stamped in gray and gold. Top edge yellow. Blue endpapers. Printed dust jacket.

The
MANSION
William Faulkner

RANDOM HOUSE · NEW YORK

Title page of No. 139

On copyright page: "First Printing."
First edition, first printing.

142 ——. New York: Random House, [1964]. "Third printing"; first printing as part of the Snopes Trilogy.

143 ——. New York: Vintage Books (Random House), [1965]. First paperback edition.

American Excerpts

"By the People." See 562–564 this title, 1955–1960.

144 "Mink Snopes." *Esquire*, LII, No. 6 (December 1959).

Illustrations of MSS, Typescripts, Etc.

145 Two photographs on 9½″ x 11½″ mounts reproducing pp. 1 and 2 of the typesetting copy of *The Mansion*.

Reproduction of p. 1 of typescript, with authorial and editorial changes. See 2791 Virginia, *William Faulkner: Man Working, 1919–1959*, 1959. See Plate XVIII.

BRITISH EDITIONS

146 *The Mansion*
   London: Chatto & Windus, 1961.
   A–M¹⁶ N⁸, 200 ll.
   pp. [1–12] 13–399 [400].
   Red boards; spine gold-stamped. Top edge red.
Printed dust jacket.
   First British edition, first printing.

TRANSLATIONS

French

147 *Le domaine*. Paris: Gallimard, 1962. Trans. René Hilleret. Copy 1: Number 36 of 66 on "vélin pur fil Lafuma–Navarre." Copy 2 and copy 3.

German

148 *Das Haus*. Stuttgart: Goverts, 1960. Trans. Elisabeth Schnack.

149 ——. Zurich: Fretz & Wasmuth, 1960. The Schnack translation.

Italian

150 *Il palazzo*. Turin: Carlo Frassinelli, 1963. Trans. Luciano Bianciardi. "Prima edizione."

Spanish

151 *La mansion*. Buenos Aires–Barcelona–Mexico City: Plaza & Janés, 1961. Trans. Jorge Ferrer-Vidal. "Primera Edición."

152 ——. Barcelona: Ediciones G. P., 1964. The Ferrer-Vidal translation.

Miscellaneous—Excerpts

153 *Mink*. Prague: SNKLU, 1963. Trans. Jiří Valja.

154 *Mosquitoes*
New York: Boni and Liveright, 1927.
The first three lines printed in blue, the rest of title page in black.
[1–22⁸], 176 ll.
pp. [i–ii] [1–8] 9–349 [350].   18.9 cm.
Blue V-cloth; yellow-stamped on front and spine. Top edge probably yellow. Blue and white floral endpapers.
Three copies in printed dust jacket. Copy 1: Inscribed by previous owner on title page "To Bill Faulkner from Bill Conselman," and signed by Faulkner, "W. Faulkner Los Ang 26 Nov 1932." Copy 2 and copy 3.
First edition, first printing.

155 ——. New York: Boni and Liveright, 1931. First edition, "Second printing, September, 1931."

156 ——. New York: Liveright, [ca. 1932].   First edition, reprint.

157 ——. Garden City: Sun Dial, 1937.   First edition, reprint.

158 ——. New York: Avon, [ca. 1942].   First edition, reprint.

159 ——. [ca. 1945].   First edition, reprint.

160 ——. New York: Liveright, [ca. 1955].   First edition, reprint.

161 ——. New York: Dell, [1953].   Second American edition, presumably first printing.

162 ——. [1956].   Second American edition, second printing.

Title page of No. 154

163 ——. 1957. Second American edition, "Third Dell printing."

164 ——. 1962. Second American edition, probably fourth printing. "New Dell edition, first printing—May 1962."

American Excerpts

"A Louisiana Sheep-Ranch."   See 516 *Twelve American Writers*, ed. William M. Gibson and George Arms, 1962.

Illustrations of MSS, Typescripts, Etc.

Reproduction of revised typescript of p. 336.   See 2768 and 2766 Meriwether, "Career" and *Career*.

BRITISH EDITIONS

165   *Mosquitoes*.   London: Chatto & Windus, 1964. Introduction by Richard Hughes.   First British edition.

TRANSLATIONS

French

166   *Moustiques*.   Paris: Éditions de Minuit, 1948. [Trans. Jean Dubramet.]   Introduction by Raymond Queneau.   Copy 1: Number 38 of 50 on "vélin supérieur de Corée."   Copy 2: Number 64 of 105 on "alfamousse des Papeteries de Navarre."   Copy 3: Printed dust jacket.   Copy 4.

167   ——.   Paris: Union General d'Éditions, 1963. The Dubramet translation.

German

168   *Moskitos*.   Hamburg: Rowohlt, 1960.   Trans. Richard K. Flesch.

Spanish

169   *Mosquitos*.   Buenos Aires: Ediciones Siglo Veinte, 1956.   Trans. Jerónimo Córdoba.

170   ——.   Barcelona: Caralt, 1959.   Trans. Domingo Manfredi.   "Primera edición."

See 1008 *Obras completas*, Vol. I, 1959.   The Manfredi translation.

Miscellaneous

171   *Snobovi*.   Belgrade: Biblioteka Minerva, 1962. Trans. into Croation by Jelena Stojanović.

172 *Pylon*

New York: Harrison Smith and Robert Haas, 1935.
The patch of sky around the plane is blue; the rest of the title page is printed in black.
[1–19⁸ 20⁶], 158 ll., 2 inserts.
pp. [1–7] 8–315 [316]. 18.9 cm.
Blue V-cloth, front and back covered with silver paper; front blue-stamped and spine silver-stamped. Top edge silver. Boxed.
Certificate of limitation: ". . . limited to 310 copies of which 300 are for sale each copy numbered and signed by the author . . . Number [ ]," tipped in facing p. [316].
Fold-out facsimile of a page of the manuscript tipped in facing the title page, p. [3].
42.4 reads "Th" in the limited, trade, and advance copies, as well as in the "Second Printing."
The trade and limited copies of this book may be separate printings, but no priority has been established.
Copy 1: Number 244. Copy 2: Number 295.
First edition, possibly first printing.

173 ——. New York: Harrison Smith and Robert Haas, [1935].
The title page is printed all in black.
[1–19⁸ 20⁶], 152 ll.
pp. [1–7] 8–315 [316].
Advance copy in printed wrappers.
On copyright page: "First Printing, February, 1935."
First edition, possibly second printing.

174 ——. New York: Harrison Smith and Ropert Haas, [1935]. Same title page, pagination, and collation as advance copy. Blue V-cloth with black band; front and spine gold-stamped. Top edge black. On copyright page: "First printing, February, 1935." Copy 1 and copy 2: Printed dust jacket. Copy 3. First edition, possibly second printing.

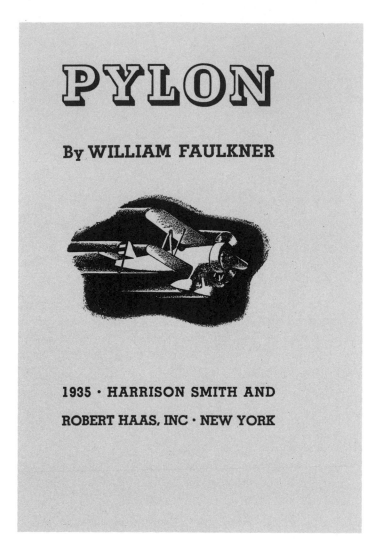

Title page of No. 172

175 ——. 1935. First edition, "second printing."

176 ——. New York: New American Library, 1951. Second American edition, "First printing."

177 ——. 1958. Second American edition, "Second printing."

178 ——. New York: Random House, [1965]. Reprint, "reproduced photographically . . . from a copy of the first printing." Three copies.

Illustrations of MSS, Typescripts, Etc.

Reproduction of MS page, unnumbered. See 2768 and 2766 Meriwether, "Career" and *Career*.

BRITISH EDITIONS

179 *Pylon*
    London: Chatto & Windus, 1935.
    [A]⁴ B–X⁸, 164 ll.
    pp. [i–vi] vii [viii] 1–318 [319–320].
    Laid paper. Red V-cloth; spine white-stamped. Printed dust jacket.
    First British edition, first printing.

180 ——. London: Lehmann, 1950. Second British edition, first printing.

181 ——. London: New Phoenix Library (Chatto & Windus), 1954. Second British edition, reprint.

182 ——. London: Chatto & Windus, 1955. Second British edition, reprint.

TRANSLATIONS

French

183 *Pylone*. Paris: Gallimard, 1946. Trans. R-N. Raimbault and Mme G. Louis-Rousselet. Copy 1: Number LXIV of 105 on "vélin pur Lafuma Navarre." Copy 2: Number 879 of 1,040 on ordinary paper in a binding designed by Mario Prassinos.

German

184 *Wendemarke*. Hamburg: Rowohlt, 1951. Trans. Georg Goyert. "Rororo Taschenbuch Ausgabe veröffenlicht Februar 1951."

Italian

185 *Oggi si vola*. Milan: Mondadori, 1937. Trans. with introduction by Lorenzo Gigli.

Spanish

186 *Pylon*. Barcelona: Caralt, 1947. Trans. Julio Fernández-Yáñez. "Primera edición."

See 1009 *Obras escogidas*, Vol. I, 1956, and 1008 *Obras completas*, Vol. II, 1962. The Fernández-Yáñez translation in both.

Miscellaneous

187 *Trekanten*. Copenhagen: Fonss, [ca. 1952]. Trans. Peter Toubro.

188 *Pylon*. Copenhagen: Spektrum, [1963]. The Toubro translation previously published under the title *Trekanten*.

189 *Sora no yūwaku*. Tokyo: Dabiddosha, 1958. Trans. Kensaburo Chashi. Second edition.

See 1012 *Shino tokoni yo kotawannte*, 1959. Trans. Masami Nishikawa.

190 *Potamneli andjeli*. Belgrade: Kosmos, 1961. Trans. into Croatian by Branka Petrović. Cinema version.

191 *Luftcirkus*. Stockholm: Bonniers, 1961. Trans. Nils A. Bengtsson. Copy 1: Blue V-cloth, gold-stamped on spine and front; printed dust jacket same as paperback. Copy 2 and copy 3: Paperback.

192   *The Reivers: A Reminiscence.*
New York: Random House, [1962].
[1–10¹⁶], 160 ll., 1 insert.
pp. [i–viii] [1–3] 4–305 [306–312]. 25 cm.
Laid paper. Maroon V-cloth; front and spine gold-stamped. Top edge red. Green endpapers.
Certificate of limitation: ". . . five hundred copies. . . . Each copy is signed by the author and numbered. 313]," tipped in facing p. [ii].
On copyright page: "First Printing."
The limited and trade copies are from the same printing.
First edition, first printing.

193   ——. New York: Random House, [1962].
Same title page as limited copy.
[1–10¹⁶], 160 ll.
pp. [i–viii] [1–3] 4–305 [306–312].
Wove paper. Red V-cloth; front and spine stamped in orange and gold. Top edge red. Gold endpapers.
On copyright page: "First Printing."
Three copies in printed dust jacket. Copy 1. Copy 2: Book-of-the-Month Club brochure laid in. Copy 3: Presentation copy inscribed on endpaper, "To Mrs. Ethel Moore sincerely William Faulkner Charlottesville 27 May 1962," and signed on title page, "William Faulkner."
First edition, first printing.

194   ——. New York: Random House, [1962]. First edition, "third printing."

195   ——. [1962]. First edition, "fourth printing."

196   ——. [1963?]. Printing "W."

American Excerpts

197   "Hell Creek Crossing." *Saturday Evening Post,* CCXXXV, No. 13 (March 31, 1962).

198   "The Education of Lucius Priest." *Esquire,* LVII, No. 5 (May 1962).

THE
REIVERS
A Reminiscence
WILLIAM
FAULKNER

RANDOM HOUSE
New York

Title page of No. 192

BRITISH EDITIONS

199 *The Reivers*
London: Chatto & Windus, 1962.
[A]⁸ B–S⁸, 144 ll.
pp. [1–7] 8–284 [285–288].
Blue boards; spine gold-stamped. Printed dust jacket.
First British edition, first printing.

200 ——. London: Chatto & Windus, 1962. First British edition, "Second Impression September 1962."

OTHER FOREIGN EDITIONS IN ENGLISH— EXCERPTS

201 "Hell Creek Crossing." *Reader's Digest Condensed Books.* Tokyo: Reader's Digest of Japan, 1964.

TRANSLATIONS

French

202 *Les larrons.* Paris: Gallimard, 1964. Trans. Maurice-E. Coindreau and Raymond Girard. With preface by Raymond Girard. Copy 1: Number 33 of 67 on "vélin pur Lafuma-Navarre." Copy 2 and copy 3: Trade edition.

203 ——. [1964]. The Coindreau and Girard translation, with preface by Girard. Collection Soleil, Number 177 of 3100 copies.

German

204 *Die Spitzbuben.* Stuttgart: Goverts, 1963. Trans. Elisabeth Schnack.

205 ——. Zurich: Fretz & Wasmuth, 1963. The Schnack translation.

206 ——. *Frankfurter Allgemeine* (Frankfurt am Main), April–May 1964. The Schnack translation. Serialized publication, various dates, in 35 parts.

Italian

207 *I saccheggiatori.* Milan: Mondadori, Club degli Editori, [1963?]. Trans. Giorgio Monicelli.

208 ——. Milan: Mondadori, 1963. The Monicelli translation. "I edizione Settembre 1963."

Spanish

209 *Los rateros.* Buenos Aires–Barcelona–Mexico City–Bogotá–Rio de Janeiro: Plaza & Janés, 1963. Trans. Jorge Ferrer-Vidal Turull. "Primera edición."

210 ——. Barcelona: Ediciones G. P., [1964]. The Ferrer-Vidal Turull translation.

Miscellaneous

211 *Os desgarrados.* Rio de Janeiro: Editôra Civilização Brasileira, 1963. Trans. Breno Silveira. Copy 1: Number 01832. Copy 2: Number 05780.

212 *Tre rövare.* Stockholm: Bonniers, 1963. Trans. Gunnar Barklund.

213 *De Rovers.* Utrecht: A. W. Bruna en Zoon, 1963. Trans. John Vandenbergh.

214 *Tyveknektene.* Oslo: Gyldendal, 1964. Trans. Leo Strøm.

215 *Os ratoneiros.* Lisbon: Portugália, [1964]. Trans. with preface by Manuel Barbosa.

216 *Zsiványok.* Budapest: Európa Könyvkiadó, 1965. Trans. into Hungarian by László Szíjgyártó.

217 *Requiem for a Nun.* Galley proof. Set No. 1, complete.

218 ——. Galley proof. Set No. 2. Galleys 1–69 A, 70–93 A. Acts I–III in blue covers with printed label on front. "The Jail" in gray front cover with typed label.

219 *Requiem for a Nun*
  New York: Random House, [1951].
  Gray title page; title and publisher's emblem in white, the rest printed in black.
  [1¹⁸ 2–9¹⁶], 146 ll., 1 insert.
  pp. [i–vi] [1–2] 3–286. 20.3 cm.
  Laid paper. Black V-cloth, front and back covered with marbled paper; spine gold-stamped. Top edge gray. Gray endpapers.
  Certificate of limitation: ". . . limited to seven hundred and fifty copies, signed by the author Number ——," tipped in before p. [i].

  This printing has thirty-five misprints which are corrected in later printings:

21.3	Chocktaw	[Choctaw
24.23	lock,	[lock.
37.18	track	[tract
46.22	concomitant	[concomitant
48.6	infinitestimal	[infinitesimal
50.12,15	five	[two
95.6	exists	[exits
95.22	Three two	[Two three
104.18	millenium's	[millennium's
105.25	dispossed	[dispossessed
107.24	enchanelled	[enchannelled
109.20	1844	[1884
130.20	gentlemen	[gentleman
155.25	Is	[It
214.11	calsomine	[calcimine
217.25	stage its	[stage enthroned on its
223.16	sheathe	[sheath
226.12	girt	[girth
228.17	cousins	[cousin
236.2	not	[now
248.28	evening	[even
256.4	cabable	[capable
257.2	job	[jog
257.12	pillon	[pillion
258.10	pillon	[pillion
259.28	lost	[loss
266.3	critcism	[criticism
269.10,24	ten	[thirty
274.18	five	[eight
277.13	five	[eight
280.4	five	[eight
277.9	why	[Why
278.21	he	[He

  The trade and limited copies are from the same printing.
  Copy 1: Number 590. Copy 2: Number 655.
  First edition, first printing.

220 ——. New York: Random House, [1951].
  Same title page as limited copy, but tan with white and black lettering.
  [1¹⁸ 2–9¹⁶], 146 ll.
  pp. [i–vi] [1–2] 3–286.
  Wove paper. Green V-cloth covers and black V-cloth shelfback; spine gold-stamped. Top edge dark gray. White endpapers.
  With all misprints noted in the limited copy.
  Two copies in printed dust jacket. Copy 1: Contemporary reviews laid in. Copy 2.
  First edition, first printing.

221 ——. New York: Random House, [1951]. The following misprints have been corrected: 24.23; 46.22; 48.6; 50.12,15; 109.20; 217.25; 236.2; 257.2; 269.10,24. First edition, "Second Printing."

222 ——. [1951]. All the misprints noted in the limited printing have been corrected. First edition, "Third Printing."

Title page of No. 219

225　"A Name for the City."　*Harper's Magazine Centennial Issue*, CCI (October 1950).

226　"The Jail."　*Partisan Review*, XVIII, No. 5 (September–October 1951).

227　"A Name for a City."　*Prize Stories of 1951, The O. Henry Awards*, ed. Herschel Brickell.　Garden City: Doubleday, 1951.

"The Courthouse."　See 443 *The Faulkner Reader*, 1954, and related entries.

Illustrations of MSS, Typescripts, Etc.

Reproduction of a galley with authorial revisions.　See 2766 Meriwether, *Career*.

BRITISH EDITIONS

228　*Requiem for a Nun*
　　London: Chatto & Windus, 1953.
　　[A]⁸ B–Q⁸, 128 ll.
　　pp. [1–8] 9–251 [252–256].
　　Blue boards; spine gold-stamped.　Printed dust jacket.
　　First British edition, first printing.

229　——.　Harmondsworth: Penguin, 1960.　Second British edition, first printing.

British Excerpts

"The Courthouse."　See 445 *Faulkner's County*, 1955.

TRANSLATIONS

French

See 242 *Requiem pour une nonne*, 1956.　Adapted by Albert Camus.

230　*Requiem pour une nonne*.　Paris: Gallimard, 1957.　Trans. M.-E. Coindreau.　Preface by Albert Camus.

223　Sanctuary *and* Requiem for a Nun.　New York: New American Library, 1954.　A new setting of both novels.　First joint edition, first printing.

224　——.　1961.　First joint edition, fourth printing.　Two copies.

Excerpts

"Un nom pour la ville." See 1006 *Jefferson, Mississippi*, 1956. The Coindreau translation.

German

231 *Requiem für eine Nonne*. Zurich: Fretz & Wasmuth, 1956. Trans. Robert Schnorr.

232 ——. Stuttgart: Goverts, 1956. The Schnorr translation. Two copies.

See 245 *Requiem für eine Nonne*, n.d. The Schnorr translation.

233 *Requiem für eine Nonne*. Munich: Deutscher Taschenbuch Verlag, [October 1964]. The Schnorr translation.

Title page of No. 241

Italian

234 *Requiem per una monaca.* Milan: Mondadori, 1955. Trans. Fernanda Pivano. "I Edizione."

See 243 *Requiem per una monaca,* 1959. The Camus adaptation. Trans. Luciano Lucignani.

See 1007 *Tutte le opere di William Faulkner,* Vol. VI, 1963. The Pivano translation.

235 *Requiem per una monaca.* Milan: Mondadori, "I edizione il bosco maggio 1964." The Pivano translation.

236 ——. 1964. The Pivano translation.

Excerpts

"Il tribunale" and "La prigione." See 498 *664 pagine di William Faulkner,* 1959.

Spanish

237 *Requiem para una mujer.* Buenos Aires: Emecé, 1956. Trans. Jorge Zalamea. "Segunda edición."

238 ——. 1962. "Cuarta edición."

See 244 *Requiem para una reclusa,* 1960. The Camus adaptation. Trans. Victoria Ocampo.

Miscellaneous

239 *Sjalamässa för en nunna.* Stockholm: Bonniers, 1952. Trans. Mårten Edlund.

240 *Requiem por uma freira.* Lisbon: Gleba, 1959. Trans. with introduction by Luis de Sousa Rebelo. Number 864 of 1,500 "impressa em papel offset GG."

DRAMATIC ADAPTATIONS

By Ruth Ford

241 *Requiem for a Nun:* A Play from the novel by William Faulkner adapted to the stage by Ruth Ford.
    New York: Random House, [1959].
    Two-page photographic title.
    [1–4^{16}], 64 ll., 4 inserts.
    pp. [i–xii] [1–2] 3–105 [106–112]. 20.4 cm.
    Gray boards; front and spine stamped in gold and black; photograph pasted on front cover. Top edge yellow. Printed dust jacket.
    Two-leaf photographic title inserted after p. [vi]; single photographic leaves facing pp. 56 and 78.
    On copyright page: "First Printing."
    First edition, first printing.

By Albert Camus

242 *Requiem pour une nonne.* Paris: Gallimard, 1956. Number 28 of 75 on "vélin pur fil Lafuma-Navarre."

243 *Requiem per una monaca. Sipario* (Milan), No. 153 (January 1959). Trans. Luciano Lucignani.

244 *Requiem par una reclusa.* Buenos Aires: Sur, [1960]. Trans. Victoria Ocampo.

———————

245 *Requiem für eine Nonne,* Frankfurt: Fischer, n.d. Trans. Robert Schnorr. Mimeographed acting version.

246 *Sanctuary*. Galley proof of the original, unrevised version. Galleys 1–103.

247 ——. New York: Jonathan Cape and Harrison Smith, 1930. Salesman's dummy. [1⁴], 4 ll. pp. [i–iv] 1–4. Magenta and gray boards with gold-stamped V-cloth shelfback. Endpapers same pattern as boards. Printed dust jacket. On copyright page: "First published 1930." Pp. 1–4 have the text of the unrevised version of the novel.

248 ——. Unbound gatherings of the first printing with holograph corrections by the author and with editorial notes. The author's marked copy.

249 *Sanctuary*
New York: Jonathan Cape and Harrison Smith, [1931].
[1–24⁸], 192 ll.
pp. [i–iv] 1–380. 18.6 cm.
Magenta boards, with red-stamped gray V-cloth shelfback. Top edge gray. Magenta and white endpapers with geometrical design.
On copyright page: "First Published, 1931."
Four copies, copies 1–3 in printed dust jacket. Copy 1: Inscribed on title page, "A heeltap to Bill Conselman Wm Faulkner Los Angeles, Cal 26 May 1932." Copies 2–4. All four copies have the red and white endpapers; the second and later printings in this collection have magenta endpapers with the same pattern as the boards.
First edition, first printing.

250 ——. New York: Cape & Smith, [1931]. In the text of the second printing: 211.8 were [where]. Copy 1 and copy 2: No dust jacket. First edition, "second printing, February, 1931."

251 ——. 1931. Copy 1 and copy 2: No dust jacket. First edition, "third printing, February, [1931]."

SANCTUARY

WILLIAM
FAULKNER

NEW YORK
JONATHAN CAPE & HARRISON SMITH

Title page of No. 249

252 ——. 1931. Three copies, with the sixteen corrections which first appeared in the fourth printing in March. First edition, "fifth printing, April, [1931]."

253 ——. [1931]. First edition, "sixth printing, July, 1931."

254 ——. New York: Modern Library, [1932].
[1–12^{16} 13^4], 196 ll.
pp. [i–iv] v–vi 1–38 [381–386].
Blue or green V-cloth; gold-stamped on front and spine. Top edge blue or green. Tan and white endpapers.
On copyright page: "First Modern Library Edition 1932."
A reprint of the original setting, but with the addition of Faulkner's "Introduction," pp. v–vi. This is the first appearance of the introduction.
Copy 1, copy 2, and copy 4: Printed dust jacket. Copy 3.
First edition, reprint.

255 ——. New York: Modern Library, [ca. 1932]. The statement, "First Modern Library Edition 1932" has been removed, and the introduction has been reset on pp. v–viii. The binding cloths are variant, and the impressions from the plates in this state are multiple. First edition, reprint. Three copies.

256 ——. New York: Smith & Haas, 1931 [ca. 1932]. On copyright page: "Sixth Printing, July, 1931"—but later than the Cape & Smith sixth printing, because this Smith & Haas printing has the Modern Library introduction on four pages. Letter from Kenneth Godfrey (formerly of Smith & Haas) in regard to the above laid in. Photostats of pp. ii–iv, v. First edition, reprint.

257 ——. New York: Modern Library, [ca. 1940]. 379.17: Massanet [Massenet]. Gray B-cloth; front and spine stamped red and gold. Top edge red. Gray and white figured endpapers. Printed dust jacket.

258 ——. New York: Grosset & Dunlap, [ca. 1946]. Copy 1: With printed dust jacket. Copy 2. First edition, reprint.

259 ——. New York: Modern Library, [ca. 1951]. Blue B-cloth; front and spine stamped red and gold. Top edge red. Gray and white figured endpapers. Copy 1: Printed dust jacket. Copy 2. First edition, reprint.

260 ——. New York: Random House, [1958]. First edition, reprint.

261 ——. New York: Penguin, 1947. Second American edition, first printing. Three copies.

262 ——. New York: New American Library, 1949. Second American edition, ninth printing.

Sanctuary and Requiem for a Nun. See 223 and 224 this title, 1954 and 1961.

263 *Sanctuary.* New York: Random House, [1962]. The text has been corrected. Fourth American edition, first printing.

American Excerpts

"Uncle Bud and the Three Madams." See 494 *The Portable Faulkner,* ed. Malcolm Cowley, 1946, and related entries.

Illustrations of MSS, Typescripts, Etc.

Reproduction of first MS page, first version. See 2769 and 2766 Meriwether, "Check List" and *Career.*

Reproduction of MS p. 131, first version. See 2768 and 2766 Meriwether, "Career" and *Career.*

Reproduction of a revised galley. See 2790 Texas, *William Faulkner: An Exhibition of Manuscripts,* 1959.

BRITISH EDITIONS

264 *Sanctuary*
London: Chatto & Windus, 1931.
A^2 B–U^8 X^6, 160 ll., 2 inserts.
pp. i–iv 1 316.
Laid paper. Red V-cloth; spine gold-stamped. Top edge gray. Printed dust jacket.
Two leaves of advertisements tipped in after p. 316.
The text is bowdlerized.
First British edition, first printing.

265 ——. London: Chatto & Windus, 1952. The sheets were imported from Sweden (Stockholm: Continental, 1947). The first publication in England of the full text. Second British edition, presumably first printing.

266 ——. 1957. Second British edition, reprint.

267 ——. Harmondsworth: Penguin, 1955. The bowdlerized text. Third British edition, second printing.

OTHER FOREIGN EDITIONS IN ENGLISH

268 *Sanctuary*. Paris: Crosby Continental Editions, 1932. New edition, only printing.

TRANSLATIONS

French

269 *Sanctuaire*. Paris: Gallimard, 1933. Trans. R.-N. Raimbault and Henri Delgove. Preface by André Malraux. Number 10 of 67 "hors commerce" on "alfa Navarre."

270 ——. 1958.

271 ——. 1963. Number 1,570 of 4,100 copies.

German

272 *Die Freistatt*. Zurich: Artemis, 1951. Trans. Herberth E. Herlitschaka.

273 ——. Cologne–Berlin: Kiepenheuer & Witsch, 1953. The Herlitschaka translation. "1–30 Tausend."

274 ——. Frankfurt: Ullstein, [ca. 1955]. Reprint of the Cologne edition.

Italian

275 *Santuario*. Milan: Mondadori, 1958. Trans. with introduction by Paola Ojetti Zamattio. "III Edizione."

276 ——. 1960. New edition of the Zamattio translation. "II Edizione Medusa."

See 1007 *Tutte le opere di William Faulkner*, Vol. VI, 1963. Trans. Giorgio Monicelli.

Spanish

277 ——. Madrid: Espasa-Calpe, 1934. Trans. Lino Novás Calvo. Introduction by Antonio Marichalar. "Primera edición."

See 1009 *Obras escogidas*, Vol. II, 1962. Trans. Amando Lagaro Ros.

Miscellaneous

278 *Det allerhelligste*. Copenhagen: Athenaeum, 1942. Trans. Sven Møller Kristensen.

279 *Det aller helligiste*. Oslo: Gyldendal, 1951. Trans. Leo Strøm. Foreword by Sigurd Hoel.

280 *Grijze Zomer*. The Hague: Oisterwijk, 1951. Trans. with introduction by Johan van Keulen. "Vierde, herziene druk."

281 *Det allra heligaste*. Stockholm: Bonniers, 1951. Trans. Mårten Edlund.

282 ——. 1961. New edition of the 1951 edition. "I Delfinböckerna 1961."

283 *Sankucharii*. Tokyo: Getsuyō Shobō, 1951. Trans. Masami Nishikawa and Naotaro Takiguchi.

284 ——. Tokyo: Sincho-sha, 1958. The Nishikawa and Takiguchi translation. Third edition.

285 *Svetilište*. Novi Sad: Bratsvo jedinstro, 1953. Trans. into Serbian by Milisza Mihajlović.

286 *Azyl*. Warsaw: Państwowy Instytut Wydawniczy, 1957. Trans. Zofia Kierszys.

287 *Santuário*. Lisbon: Minerva, [ca. 1958]. Trans. Marília de Vasconcelos. Two copies.

288 *Svetilište*. Belgrade: Kultura, 1963. Trans. into Croatian by Milica Mihajlović.

289 *Sartoris*
New York: Harcourt, Brace and Company, [1929].
[1–24⁸], 192 ll.
pp. [i–iv] 1–380.   18.9 cm.
Black V-cloth; red-stamped on front and spine. Top edge red.
This and all subsequent printings from the original plates have the reading, "Bendow," at 179.27.
Three copies in printed dust jackets.
First edition, first printing.

290 ——. New York: Grosset & Dunlap, [ca. 1933]. First edition, reprint.

291 ——. New York: Harcourt, Brace, 1951. First edition, reprint.

292 ——. New York: Random House, [ca. 1956]. First edition, reprint. Two copies.

293 ——. New York: New American Library, 1953. Introduction by Robert Cantwell.   Second American edition, "First Printing." Two copies.

294 ——. [1964]. Second American edition, "Sixth Printing."

Illustrations of MSS, Typescripts, Etc.

Reproduction of first MS page ("Flags in the Dust") and typescript p. 398. See 2768 and 2766 Meriwether, "Career" and *Career*.

BRITISH EDITIONS

295 *Sartoris*
London: Chatto & Windus, 1932.

SARTORIS

— ◆◆ —

WILLIAM FAULKNER

New York
HARCOURT, BRACE
AND COMPANY

Title page of No. 289

[A]⁸ B–Z⁸ AA¹⁰, 194 ll., 2 inserts.
pp. [i–vi] 7–379 [380–382].
Blue V-cloth; spine gold-stamped.   Top edge blue.
Two leaves of advertisements inserted after p. [380]. In some copies, the two leaves of ads are inserted after p. [382].
First edition, first British reprint.

296 ———. London: Chatto & Windus, 1954.   First edition, reprint.

TRANSLATIONS

French

297 *Sartoris*.   Paris: Gallimard, 1937.   Trans. R.-N. Raimbault and Henri Delgove.   Inscribed by the translators.

Excerpts

"Les fastes et les souvenirs," "Les anchois du général Pope," "Le mort de John Sartoris," and "Un aviateur du Mississippi."   See 1006 *Jefferson, Mississippi*, 1956.   The Raimbault and Delgove translation.

German

298 *Sartoris*.   Hamburg: Rowohlt, 1961.   Trans. Hermann Stresau.   "1.–5. Tausend."

Italian

299 *Sartoris*.   Milan: Garzanti, 1955.   Trans. Maria Stella Ferrari.   "Prima edizione."

Miscellaneous

300 *Sartoris*.   Lisbon: Ulisseia, 1948.   Trans. Carlos Vieira.   Introduction by Robert Cantwell.

301 ———.   Stockholm: Bonniers, 1955.   Trans. Th. Warburton.

302 ———.   Warsaw: Państwowy Instytut Wydawniczy, 1960.   Trans. Kalina Wojciechowska.

303 ———.   [1964].   New edition of the Wojciechowska translation.

304 *Soldiers' Pay*
New York: Boni and Liveright, 1926.
[1–20⁸], 160 ll.
pp. [1–6] 7–319 [320]. 18.9 cm.
Publisher's device and rules in red; the rest of the title page printed in black.
Blue V-cloth; yellow-stamped on front and spine. White and blue floral endpapers.
This and all subsequent printings from the original plates have the reading "borders on borders upon" at 60.22.
Copy 1: Signed on title page, "Faulkner Los Angeles, Cal 26 May 1932." Copy 2 and copy 3: Printed dust jacket. Copy 4.
First edition, first printing, of Faulkner's first novel.

305 ——. Garden City: Sun Dial, 1937. First edition, possibly fifth printing.

306 ——. New York: Liveright, [ca. 1950]. First edition, reprint.

307 ——. [ca. 1954]. First edition, reprint.

308 ——. New York: New American Library, 1959. Includes text of the Nobel Prize address. Second American edition, fourth printing.

American Excerpts

309 "Soldiers' Pay." *Armageddon, The World in Literature*, ed. Eugene Löhrke. New York: Cape & Smith, 1930.

Illustrations of MSS, Typescripts, Etc.

Reproduction of typescript p. 151. See 2768 and 2766 Meriwether, "Career" and *Career*.

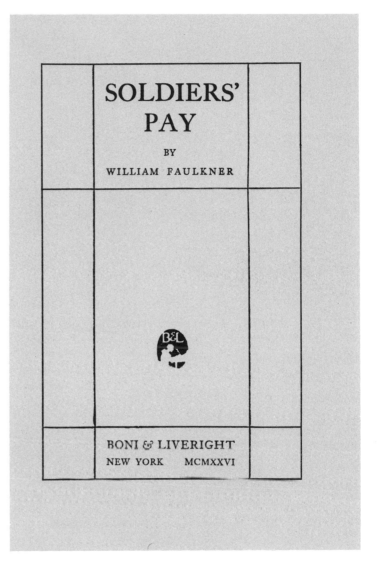

Title page of No. 304

BRITISH EDITIONS

310 *Soldiers' Pay*
London: Chatto & Windus, 1930.
Preface by Richard Hughes.
[A]⁶ B–X⁸ Y⁴, 170 ll., 2 inserts.
pp. [i–viii] ix–xi [xii] 1–326 [327–328].

Laid paper.   Green V-cloth; spine gold-stamped.
Top edge green.   Printed dust jacket.

Two leaves of advertisements tipped in after p.
[328].

The reading "borders on borders upon" is retained at
54.30.

First British edition, first printing.

311 ——.   London: Chatto & Windus, 1957.   First
British edition, probably fourth printing.

TRANSLATIONS

French

312 *Monnaie de singe*.   Grenoble–Paris: Arthaud,
1948.   Trans. with introduction by Maxime Gaucher.
Copy 1: Number 190 of 300 on "vélin à la forme B.K.F.
des Papeteries de Rives."   Copy 2: Trade edition.

German

313 *Soldatenlohn*.   Hamburg: Rowohlt, 1958.   Trans.
Susanna Rademacher.   "Rororo Taschenbuch Ausgabe
veröffenlicht im April 1958."

Italian

314 *La paga del soldato*.   Milan: Garzanti, 1953.
Trans. Massimo Alvaro.   "Prima edizione."

Spanish

315 *La paga de los soldados*.   Barcelona: Caralt, 1954.
Translator not given.   "Primera edición."

316 ——.   Mexico City: Continental, 1955.   Trans.
Francisco Gurza.

317 ——.   Buenos Aires: Schapire, [1959].   The
Gurza translation.

See 1008 *Obras completas*, Vol. I, 1959.   Translator not
given.

Miscellaneous

318 *Soldatens sold*.   Oslo: Gyldendal, 1932.   Trans.
Hans Heiberg.   Introduction by Sigurd Hoel.

319 *Soldatens lön*.   Stockholm: Bonniers, 1962.
Trans. Gunar Barklund.   Copy 1: Bound in brown
V-cloth stamped in white and black.   Copy 2: Paper-
back.

320 *Soldatens løn*.   Copenhagen: Forlaget Fremad,
1965.   Trans. Hagmund Hansen.

321 "Twilight." The first page of the holograph MS, showing the original working title of this book. See Plate II.

322 *The Sound and the Fury*
   New York: Jonathan Cape and Harrison Smith, [1929].
   [1–25⁸ 26⁴], 204 ll.
   pp. [i–vi] 1–401 [402]. 19.2 cm.
   Paper-covered boards with black, white, and gray pattern; white V-cloth shelfback; black-stamped. Top edge gray-blue. Endpapers same pattern as covers.
   On copyright page: "First Published 1929."
   Copy 1 and copy 2: Printed dust jacket.
   First edition, first printing.

The Sound and the Fury & As I Lay Dying. See 17 and 18 this title, 1946 and [ca. 1954]

323 *The Sound and the Fury*. New York: Vintage Books (Random House), [ca. 1961]. Reprint of the text in the joint edition. Paperback.

———. See 443 *The Faulkner Reader*, 1954, and related entries.

324 *The Sound and the Fury*. New York: New American Library, 1959. Third American edition, "First printing."

American Excerpts

"Dilsey." See 494 *The Portable Faulkner*, ed. Malcolm Cowley, 1946, and related entries.

325 "Sunday Morning at the Compsons." *105 Greatest Living Authors Present the World's Best*, ed. Whit Burnett. New York: Dial Press, 1950. Also galley proof of Faulkner excerpt.

THE
SOUND AND THE FURY
BY WILLIAM FAULKNER

NEW YORK
JONATHAN CAPE AND HARRISON SMITH

Title page of No. 322

II. First page of the manuscript of "Twilight," working title of *The Sound and the Fury*

See 1015 *Faulkner Reads from His Works.* Phonodisc: M-G-M, E 3617 ARC (1957).

Illustrations of MSS, Typescripts, Etc.

Reproductions of MS pp. 34 and 70. See 2768 and 2766 Meriwether, "Career" and *Career.*

Reproduction of last MS page. See 2769 and 2766 Meriwether, "Check List" and *Career.*

BRITISH EDITIONS

326 *The Sound and the Fury*
    London: Chatto & Windus, 1931.
    Introduction by Richard Hughes.
    [A]⁶ B–X⁸ Y⁴, 170 ll.
    pp. [i–vi] vii–ix [x–xii] 1–321 [322–328].
    Laid paper. Black V-cloth; spine red-stamped.
Top edge red. Printed dust jacket.
    First British edition, first printing.

327 ——. London: Chatto & Windus, 1954. First British edition, reprint.

328 ——. London: Landsborough, 1959. New edition, presumably first printing.

329 ——. London: Penguin Modern Classics, 1964. Introduction by Richard Hughes.

TRANSLATIONS

French

330 *Le bruit et la fureur.* Paris: Gallimard, [1938]. Trans. with preface by M.-E. Coindreau. Copy 1: Number 8 of 50 on "alfa des Papeteries Lafuma-Navarre." Copy 2: Inscribed by the translator.

331 ——. 1959. New edition of the Coindreau translation, with preface.

332 ——. 1963. Collection Soleil 114; Number 1,026 of 4,100.

Excerpts

"Dilsey." See 1006 *Jefferson, Mississippi,* 1956. The Coindreau translation.

German

333 *Schall und Wahn.* Zurich: Fretz & Wasmuth, 1956. Trans. Helmut M. Braem and Elisabeth Kaiser.

334 ——. Stuttgart: Scherz & Goverts, 1956. The Braem and Kaiser translation. Two copies.

335 ——. Munich: Kindler Verlag, [1964]. The Braem and Kaiser translation.

Italian

336 *L'urlo e il furore.* Milan. Mondadori, 1947. Trans. Augusto Dauphiné. "1 Edizione."

Spanish

337 *El sonido y la furia.* Buenos Aires: Libros del Mirasol, 1961. Trans. F. E. Lavalle. Contains Faulkner's "Appendix."

338 ——. 1963. Reprint of 1961 edition with translator's name changed to Floreal Mazia.

See 1009 *Obras escogidas,* Vol. II, 1962. Trans. Amando Lagaro Ros.

Miscellaneous

See 1010 *Hibiki to ikari,* 1957. Trans. Masaō Takahashi.

339 *Krik i bijes.* Zagreb: Naprijed, 1958. Trans. into Croatian. Introduction by Stjepan Krešić. Contains Faulkner's "Appendix." Two copies.

340 *Khasm va Hyahu.* Tehran: Neel, 1960. Trans. Bahman Shalavar. Copy 1: Blue Fabricord, gold-stamped front and spine, printed dust jacket. Copy 2: Paperback with printed dust jacket.

341 *O som e a fúria.* Lisbon: Portugália, [1960?]. Trans. Mario Henrique Leiria and H. Santos Carvalho. Preface by Luis de Sousa Rebelo.

342 *Um-hyang kwa bun-no.* Seoul: Jung um Sah, 1961. Trans. In-sup Jung. Contains also *The Unvanquished.*

343 [*The Sound and the Fury.*] Beirut: Dar el-Ilm Lil-Malayeen, [1963]. Trans. into Arabic by Jabra I. Jabra.

344 *Stormen och vreden.* Stockholm: Bonniers, [1964]. Trans. Gunnar Barklund.

345   *The Town.*   Galley proof.   Galleys [2–4] 5–119.

346   *The Town*
New York: Random House, [1957].
The author's name in red, the rest of the title page printed in black.
[1–12¹⁶], 192 ll., 1 insert.
pp. [i–viii] [1–3] 4–371 [372–376]. 20.4 cm.
Laid paper.   Tan V-cloth; gold-stamped on front and spine.   Top edge red.   Yellow-tan endpapers.
Certificate of limitation: ". . . limited to four hundred and fifty copies.   Number [367]," tipped in before p. [i].
On copyright page: "First Printing."
In both the trade and the limited "First Printing," 327.8 is repeated at line 10.
The limited and trade copies are from the same printing.
First edition, first printing.

347   ——.   New York: Random House, [1957].
The title page is printed all in black.
[1–12¹⁶], 192 ll.
pp. [i–viii] [1–3] 4–371 [372–376].
Wove paper.   Red V-cloth; front and spine stamped in gray and gold.   Top edge gray.   Gray endpapers.
On copyright page: "First Printing."
Five copies in printed dust jacket.   Copy 3: Tan V-cloth, front and spine stamped in black and green. Top edge unstained.
First edition, first printing.

348   ——.   New York: Random House, [1957].   First edition, "Second Printing."

349   ——.   New York: Vintage Books (Random House), 1961.   Pp. 368–371 reset.   The first paragraph on p. 368 has been rewritten to change Clarence Snopes

The
TOWN
William Faulkner

RANDOM HOUSE · NEW YORK

Title page of No. 346

to Doris Snopes.   "First vintage Edition."   Two copies.

350   ——.   New York: Random House, 1964.

"Fourth printing," first printing as part of the Snopes Trilogy.

American Excerpts

351 "The Waifs." *Saturday Evening Post*, CCXXIX, No. 44 (May 4, 1957).

352 ——. *Saturday Evening Post Stories 1957*. New York: Random House, 1957.

Illustrations of MSS, Typescripts, Etc.

Reproduction of two corrected galleys. See 2769 and 2766 Meriwether, "Check List" and *Career*.

BRITISH EDITIONS

353 *The Town*
    London: Chatto & Windus, 1958.
    A–K¹⁶, 160 ll.
    pp. [1–7] 8–319 [320].
    Red boards; spine gold-stamped. Printed dust jacket.
    First British edition, first printing.

TRANSLATIONS

French

354 *La ville*. Paris: Gallimard, 1962. Trans. J. and L. Bréant. Copy 1: Number 12 of 66 on "vélin pur fil Lafuma-Navarre." Copy 2: Trade edition.

355 ——. 1962. Collection Soleil.

356 ——. 1963. Number 2,624 of 4,100 copies.

German

357 *Die Stadt*. Zurich: Fretz & Wasmuth, 1958. Trans. Elisabeth Schnack.

Italian

358 *La città*. Milan: Mondadori, 1961. Trans. Giorgio Monicelli and Bruno Tasso. "1 Edizione."

Spanish

359 *En la ciudad*. Buenos Aires–Barcelona–Mexico City: Plaza & Janés, 1960. Trans. Ramon Hernandez. "Primera edición."

360 ——. Barcelona: Ediciones G. P., 1960. Trans. Ramon Hernandez, here printed as "Fernandez." Volume includes works by other authors.

361 ——. Barcelona: Ediciones Cisne, 1963. The Hernandez translation.

Miscellaneous

362 *Staden*. Stockholm: Bonniers, 1958. Trans. Pelle Fritz-Crone.

363 *Grad*. Zagreb: Mladost, 1959. Trans. into Croatian with appendix by Branko Brusar.

364 *The Unvanquished*
New York: Random House, [1938].
First and last lines on title page in red, the rest printed in black.
[1–19⁸], 152 ll., 1 insert.
pp. [i–viii] [1–2] 3–293 [294–296]. 20.4 cm.
Wove paper watermarked "Archer." Front and back covered with printed paper, red V-cloth shelfback; spine gold-stamped. Top edge gold.
Certificate of limitation: ". . . limited to two hundred and fifty copies . . . signed by the author. Number [82]," tipped in facing p. [ii].
On copyright page: "First Printing."
The trade and limited copies are from the same printing.
First edition, first printing.

365 ——. New York: Random House, [1938].
Same title page as the limited printing.
[1–19⁸], 152 ll.
pp. [i–viii] [1–2] 3–293 [294–296].
Unwatermarked paper. Gray V-cloth; front and spine stamped in red and blue. Top edge red. Printed dust jacket.
On copyright page: "First printing."
First edition, first printing.

366 ——. New York: Random House, [1965]. Reprint, "reproduced photographically from . . . a copy of the first printing."

367 ——. New York: New American Library, 1952. Second American edition, "First printing." Two copies.

368 ——. 1958. Second American edition, "Second printing."

369 ——. 1959. Foreword by Carvel Collins. Third American edition, "First Signet Classics Edition."

WILLIAM FAULKNER
★
THE
UNVANQUISHED

Drawings by
Edward Shenton

★
RANDOM HOUSE   NEW YORK

Title page of No. 364

American Excerpts

"Raid." See 494 *The Portable Faulkner*, ed. Malcolm Cowley, 1946, and related entries.

"An Odor of Verbena." See 500 *A Rose for Emily and other stories*, 1945, and 443 *The Faulkner Reader*, 1954, and related entries.

BRITISH EDITIONS

370 *The Unvanquished*. London: Chatto & Windus, 1960. Reprint by photo-offset from the first British edition of 1938.

371 ——. Harmondsworth: Penguin, 1955. Second British edition, first printing.

OTHER FOREIGN EDITIONS IN ENGLISH—EXCERPTS

372 *The Unvanquished*. Bielefeld–Berlin–Hanover: Velhagen & Klasing, [1957]. Abridged text in English; foreword and notes in German.

TRANSLATIONS
French

373 *L'invaincu*. Paris: Gallimard, 1949. Trans. R.-N. Raimbault and Ch.-P. Vorce. Copy 1: Copy E of 5 "hors commerce sur vélin pur fil Lafuma-Navarre." Copy 2: Number LVII of 205 on the same paper.

Excerpts

"Une odeur de verveine." See 1006 *Jefferson, Mississippi*, 1956. The Raimbault and Vorce translation.

German

374 *Die Unbesiegten*. Zurich: Fretz & Wasmuth, 1954. Trans. with foreword by Erich Franzen. "Erstmalig in der Fischer Bücherei." Two dust jackets.

375 ——. Frankfurt–Hamburg: Fischer, 1957. New edition of the Franzen translation. Two copies.

Italian

376 *Gli invitti*. Milan: Mondadori, 1948. Trans. Alberto Marmont. "1 Edizione."

See 1007 *Tutte le opere di William Faulkner*, Vol. III–IV, 1961. Trans. Alberto Marmont.

Spanish

377 *Los invictos*. Barcelona: Caralt, 1951. Trans. Alberto Vilá de Avilés. "Primera edición."

See 1009 *Obras escogidas*, Vol. I, 1956, and 1008 *Obras completas*, Vol. II, 1962. The Vilá de Avilés translation in both.

Miscellaneous

378 *De Familie Sartoris*. Haarlem: Spaarnestad, [ca. 1938]. Translator not given.

379 *Taskhīr nā Pazīr*. Tehran: Amīr Kabīr, 1956. Trans. Parvīz Dāriūsh.

380 *Nepřemoženi*. Prague: Naše Vojsko, 1958. Trans. Josef Schwarz.

381 *Os invencidos*. Lisbon: Minerva, 1960. Trans. Abel Marques Ribeiro.

382 *Niepokonane*. Warsaw: Państwowy Instytut Wydawniczy, 1961. Trans. Ewa Życieńska.

See 342 *Um-hyang kwa bun-no*, 1961. Trans. In-sup Jung.

383 *Onoverwinnelijk*. Utrecht: A. W. Bruna en Zoon, [1964]. Trans. Dick Bruna.

384 [*The Unvanquished*.] Tel Aviv: Am Oved, 1964. Trans. into Hebrew.

385 *De obesegrade*. Stockholm: Tidens Bokklubb, [1965]. Trans. Hakan Norlén.

386 *The Wild Palms*
New York: Random House, [1939].
The wavy lines in green, the rest of the title page printed in black.
[1–21⁸ 22⁴], 172 ll., 1 insert.
pp. [i–iv] [1–2] 3–339 [340]. 20.3 cm.
Laid paper. Paper-covered boards, gold-stamped red V-cloth shelfback. Top edge gold.
Certificate of limitation: '. . . limited to two hundred and fifty copies . . . signed by the author. Number ——," tipped in before p. [i].
On copyright page: "First Printing."
The trade and limited copies are from the same printing.
Copy 1: Number 44. Copy 2: Number 189.
First edition, first printing.

387 ——. New York: Random House, [1939].
Same title page as limited printing.
[1–21⁸ 22⁴], 172 ll.
pp. [i–iv] [1–2] 3–339 [340].
Printed wrappers.
On copyright page: "First Printing."
Advance copy.
First edition, first printing.

388 ——. New York: Random House, [1939].
Same title as limited printing.
Same collation and pagination as advance copy.
Wove paper. Tan V-cloth; front and spine stamped in gold and green. Top edge green. Printed dust jacket.
On copyright page: "First Printing."
Copy 1 and copy 2: Printed dust jacket. Copy 3 and copy 4.
First edition, first printing.

389 ——. New York: Random House, n.d. First edition, "Fifth printing."

THE
WILD PALMS

by William Faulkner

RANDOM HOUSE · NEW YORK

Title page of No. 386

390 ——. First edition, "Sixth printing."

391 ——. [1962]. First edition, "Eighth printing."

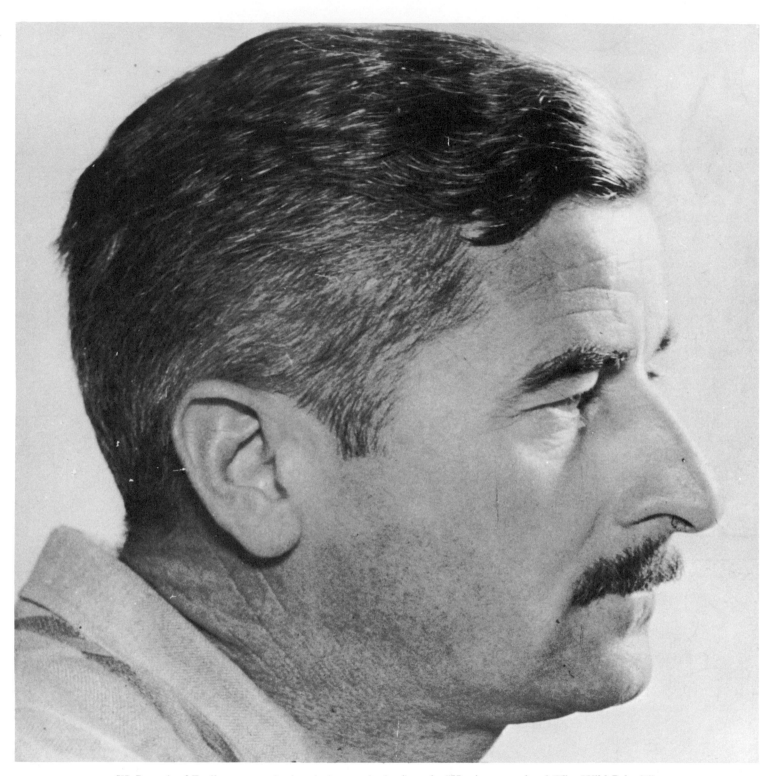

III. Portrait of Faulkner, 1939. An inscription on the back reads, "Has just completed 'The Wild Palms'?"

392 ——. New York: Vintage Books (Random House, [1964]. "First Vintage Edition, September 1964."

THE WILD PALMS AND *OLD MAN*
PRINTED AS SEPARATE WORKS

Old Man. See 494 *The Portable Faulkner*, ed. Malcolm Cowley, 1946, and related entries.

393 *The Wild Palms.* New York: Penguin, 1948. Does not include *Old Man.* Second American edition, first printing. Paperback.

394 *The Old Man* [sic]. New York: New American Library, 1948. Does not include *The Wild Palms.* Second American edition, "First printing." Paperback. Two copies.

395 The Wild Palms *and* The Old Man [*sic*]. New York: New American Library, 1954. Both stories, printed separately. Third American edition, first printing. Paperback. Two copies.

396 ——. 1959. Third American edition, second printing. Paperback. Two copies.

Old Man. See 443 and 444 *The Faulkner Reader*, 1954 and 1959, and 515 *Three Famous Novels*, 1958.

397 "The Old Man" [*sic*]. *Ten Modern Short Novels*, ed. with commentary by Leo Hamalian and Edmond L. Volpe. New York: Putnam's, 1958.

American Excerpts

"Delta Autumn." See 494 *The Portable Faulkner*, ed. Malcolm Cowley, 1946, and related entries. Excerpt from *Old Man.*

See 1013 *Faulkner Reads from His Works*, Caedmon, TC 1035 (1954). Contains an excerpt from *The Old Man* (sic).

BRITISH EDITIONS

398 *The Wild Palms*
London: Chatto & Windus, 1939.
[A]² B–U⁸ X⁶, 160 ll.
pp. [i–iv] 1–315 [316].
Laid paper. Gray and green V-cloth with black stripe; spine stamped in green and white. Top edge green. Printed dust jacket.
First British edition, first printing.

399 ——. London: Chatto & Windus, 1954. First British edition, reprint.

400 ——. 1962. First British edition, reprint.

TRANSLATIONS

French

401 *Les palmiers sauvages.* Paris: Gallimard, 1952. Trans. with preface by M.-E. Coindreau. Copy 1: Number 92 of 100 on "vélin pur Lafuma-Navarre." Copy 2: Copy A of 7 "hors commerce" on the same paper. Copy 3: Trade edition.

402 ——. Lausanne: La Guilde du Livre, 1960. New edition of the Coindreau translation. "Exemplaire de collaborateur."

German

403 Wilde Palmen *und* Der Strom. Stuttgart: Scherz & Goverts, 1957. Trans. Helmut M. Braem and Elisabeth Kaiser. Includes a German translation of Faulkner's remarks in the *Paris Review* (Spring 1956) about the two stories.

404 ——. Zurich: Fretz & Wasmuth, 1957. Same as the Stuttgart publication.

405 *Der Strom.* Frankfurt–Hamburg: Fischer, 1961. The Braem and Kaiser translation of *Old Man.* "Erstmalig in der Fischer Bücherei."

Italian

406 *Palme selvagge*.   Milan: Mondadori,   1956. Trans. Bruno Fonzi.   "1 Edizione."

Spanish

407 *Las palmeras salvajes*.   Buenos Aires: Sudamericana, 1956.   Trans. Jorge Luis Borges.   "Quinta edición."

Miscellaneous

408 *De vilde palmer*.   Copenhagen: Athenaeum, 1939. Trans. Niels Haislund and Sven Møller Kristensen.

409 *Yasei no jōnetsu*.   Tokyo: Mikasa Shobō, 1951. Trans. Yasuo Okubo.   Fourth edition.

410 *Ya-sang ui jung-yul*.   Seoul: Sum moon Kag, 1958.   Trans. Sung Hoon Park.

411 *Dzikie Palmy / Stary*.   Warsaw: Czytelnik, 1958. Trans. Kalina Wojciechowska.

412 *Divje palme*.   Ljubljana: Državna založba Slovenije, 1959.   Trans. into Croatian by Herbert Grün.

413 *Palmeiras bravas*.   Lisbon: Portugália, [1960]. Trans. with preface and notes by Jorge de Sena.   Does not include *Old Man*.

414 *O homen e o rio*.   Lisbon: Portugália, [1960?]. Trans. with preface by Luis de Sousa Rebelo.   Does not include *The Wild Palms*.

415 *Divoké palmy*.   Prague: Mladá   Fronta,   1960. Trans. Jiří Valja.

416 [*The Wild Palms*.]   P'ing-tung (Taiwan): Pai Sha Shu Wu, 1960.   Trans. Wen-Yüan Sha.

417 *Divlje palme / Starec*.   Belgrade: Prosveta, 1961. *The Wild Palms*, trans. into Serbian by Ljubica Bauer;

Old Man by Marija Djordjevich.   Also other editions of 1962, 1963, and 1966.

418 *Az öreg*.   Budapest: Európa Könyvkiadó, 1962. Trans. László Nagy.   Does not include *The Wild Palms*.

419 *De vilda palmerna*.   Stockholm: Bonniers, 1962. Trans. Mårten Edlund.

420 [*Old Man.*]   Delhi: Star Publications, 1964. Trans. into Hindi.   Contains also *The Wild Palms*.

SHORT story entries are divided into two categories: collected and selected editions of Faulkner's short stories and short stories published separately. In both categories entries are alphabetical by title. Listed with the single stories are the typescript of an unpublished story, "A Portrait of Elmer," and two typescripts (one incomplete) of published stories, "Idyll in the Desert" and "There Was a Queen." See Section IX, "Collected Editions," for collections including short stories as well as novels and other material.

COLLECTED AND SELECTED EDITIONS

ABENDSONNE

421 *Abendsonne: Drei Erzählungen.* Munich: Piper, 1956. Trans. Erich Franzen. In addition to "That Evening Sun" the book contains "Red Leaves" and "Dry September." Two copies.

BIG WOODS

422 *Big Woods.* Galley proof. "Bank 27, Galleys 90, 92–121; Bank L3, Galleys 231, 233–235, 237–40; Bank L2, Galleys 191–218."

423 ——. Page proof. 209 leaves. Orange paper covers, printed label on front.

424 *Big Woods*
    New York: Random House, [1955].
    Two-page title. The forest is printed in brown, the rest in black.
    [1–14⁸], 112 ll.
    pp. [i–x] [1–10] 11–198 [199–214]. 22.9 cm.
    Laid paper. Green V-cloth; front and spine stamped in gold and black. Top edge green. Beige endpapers. Printed dust jacket.
    On copyright page: "First Printing."
    All the material had appeared previously. Contains "The Bear," "The Old People," "A Bear Hunt," and "Race at Morning."
    First edition, first printing.

TRANSLATIONS

German

425 *Der grosse Wald.* Stuttgart: Goverts, 1964. Trans. Hermann Stresau and Elisabeth Schnack.

Miscellaneous

426 *Wielki Las.* Warsaw: Państwowy Instytut Wydawniczy, 1962. Trans. Zofia Kierszys and Jan Zakrzewski.

COLLECTED STORIES OF WILLIAM FAULKNER

427 *Collected Stories of William Faulkner*
    New York: Random House, [1950].
    [1⁸ 2–28¹⁶], 472 ll.
    pp. [i–vi] [1–2] 3–900 [901–906]. 21 cm.
    First two lines of title page in black against a blue field, the rest printed in black. Gray V-cloth; spine

Title page of No. 424

stamped in blue and gold. Top edge blue. Printed dust jacket.

On copyright page: "First printing."

The forty-two stories, all of which had appeared previously, are "Barn Burning," "Shingles for the Lord," "The Tall Men," "A Bear Hunt," "Two Soldiers," "Shall Not Perish," "A Rose for Emily," "Hair," "Centaur in Brass," "Dry September," "Death Drag," "Elly," "Uncle Willy," "Mule in the Yard," "That Will Be Fine," "That Evening Sun," "Red Leaves," "A Justice," "A Courtship," "Lo!," "Ad Astra," "Victory," "Crevasse," "Turnabout," "All the Dead Pilots," "Wash," "Honor," "Dr. Martino," "Fox Hunt," "Pennsylvania Station," "Artist at Home," "The Brooch," "My Grandmother Millard," "Golden Land," "There Was a Queen," "Mountain Victory," "Beyond," "Black Music," "The Leg," "Mistral," "Divorce in Naples," and "Carcassonne."

First edition, first printing.

428 ——. New York: Random House, [ca. 1950]. First edition, "Fifth printing."

429 ——. [ca. 1950]. First edition, "Sixth printing."

430 ——. [ca. 1952]. Freak copy in the binding of Winston S. Churchill's *Closing of the Ring*. First edition, reprint.

BRITISH EDITIONS

431 *Collected Stories of William Faulkner*
London: Chatto & Windus, 1951.
Same collation and pagination as the Random House printing.
Blue V-cloth; spine gold-stamped. Top edge blue. Printed dust jacket.
Imported American sheets with British title page conjugate.
First edition, reprint.

432 *The Collected Short Stories of William Faulkner*
Vol. I. *Uncle Willy and Other Stories*. London: Chatto & Windus, 1958. Offset from *Collected Stories*. First edition, reprint.

Vol. II. *These Thirteen*. London: Chatto & Windus, 1958. Offset from *Collected Stories*. First edition, reprint.

Vol. III. *Dr. Martino and Other Stories*. London: Chatto & Windus, 1958. Offset from *Collected Stories*. First edition, reprint. Two copies.

Title page of No. 427

TRANSLATIONS—COMPLETE AND SELECTED

433 *Opowiadania.* Warsaw: Państwowy Instytut Wydawniczy, 1958. 2 vols. Vol. I: Trans. Zofia Kierszys and Jan Zakrzewski. Vol. II: Trans. Zofia Kierszys and Ewa Życieńska.

434 *Růže pro Emilii.* Prague: Státní Nakladatelství, 1958. Trans. Josef Schwarz and Zdeněk Urbánke. Afterword by Vítězslav Kocourek. Four copies. Contains, in addition to the title story, the following others from *Collected Stories:* "Lo!," "Mountain Victory," "Wash," "Barn Burning," "That Will Be Fine," "That Evening Sun," "Dry September," "A Bear Hunt," "Elly," "The Brooch," "Pennsylvania Station," "Golden Land," "Crevasse," "Ad Astra," "Victory," "Turnabout," "The Tall Men," "Two Soldiers," and "Shall Not Perish."

435 *Suchý september.* Prague: Slovenské Vydavatel'stvo Krásnej Literatúry, 1964. Trans. Josef Kot.

436 *Czerwone Liście; Opowiadania.* Warsaw: Państwowy Instytut Wydawniczy, [1964]. Trans. Zofia Kierszys, Jan Żakrzewski, and Ewa Zycieńska. Contains "Red Leaves" and other selected stories from 433 *Opowiadania.*

DOCTOR MARTINO

437   *Doctor Martino and Other Stories*
    New York: Harrison Smith and Robert Haas, 1934.
    [1–24⁸], 192 ll., 1 insert.
    pp. [i–x] 1–371 [372–374]. 20.6 cm.
    Laid paper. Red and black V-cloth; gold-stamped on front and spine. Top edge black.
    Certificate of limitation: ". . . limited to 360 copies, of which 350 are for sale. Each copy is numbered and signed by the author This is number [ ]," tipped in facing p. [372].
    The trade and limited copies of this book may be separate printings, but no priority has been established.
    First appearance of "Black Music" and "Leg." "There Was a Queen," "Death Drag," "Smoke," "Beyond," "The Hound," "Honor," "Elly," "Turnabout," "Fox Hunt," "Wash," "Mountain Victory," and the title story had previous publication.
    Copy 1: Number 139. Copy 2: Number 290.
    First edition, possibly first printing.

438 ——. New York: Harrison Smith and Robert Haas, [1934].
    Same title page as limited printing.
    [1–24⁸], 192 ll.
    pp. [i–x] 1–371 [372–374].
    Wove paper. Blue V-cloth; gold-stamped on front and spine. Top edge yellow. Printed dust jacket.
    First edition, possibly second printing.

BRITISH EDITIONS

439   *Doctor Martino*
    London: Chatto & Windus, 1934.
    [A]⁸ B–Z⁸ A2⁸ (–A2₈), 191 ll., 2 inserts.
    pp. [i–x] [1] 2–371 [372].
    Brick V-cloth; spine gold-stamped. Top edge red. Printed dust jacket.
    Two leaves of advertisements tipped in after p. [372].
    First edition, first British reprint.

TRANSLATIONS—FRENCH

440 *Le docteur Martino et autres histoires.* Paris: Gallimard, 1948. Trans. R.-N. Raimbault and Ch.-P. Vorce. Copy 1: Number LXXXIX of 210 on "vélin pur Lafuma-Navarre." Copy 2: Number 617 of 1040 on "alfa Navarre."

DOCTOR MARTINO

and other stories

by William Faulkner

NEW YORK · MCMXXXIV

HARRISON SMITH AND ROBERT HAAS

Title page of No. 437

DOKTOR MARTINO

441 *Doktor Martino: Hikâyeler*. Istanbul: Yenilik Yayinevi, 1956. Trans. Bilge Karasu. Contains "Doctor Martino," "Go Down, Moses," "Elly," and "Carcassonne."

THE FAULKNER READER

442 *The Faulkner Reader*. Galley proof. Galleys [i–ii], 1–473, 1–20, plus 3 galleys of "Foreword" laid in. Blue covers, with printed label on front.

443 *The Faulkner Reader*
New York: Random House, 1954.
[1–20^{16} 21^{12} 22^{16}], 348 ll.
pp. [i–vi] vii [viii] ix–xi [xii] [1–2] 3–682 [683–684].
Blue V-cloth; front and spine stamped in black and gold. Top edge red.
Printed dust jacket.
First appearance of the author's "Foreword." All the rest is reprinted. Contains "The Bear," "A Rose for Emily," "Barn Burning," "Dry September," "That Evening Sun," "Turnabout," "Shingles for the Lord," "A Justice," "Wash," *The Sound and the Fury, Old Man*, the Nobel Prize address, "Spotted Horses" (from *The Hamlet*, "An Odor of Verbena" (from *The Unvanquished*, "Percy Grimm" (from *Light in August*, and "The Courthouse" (from *Requiem for a Nun*).
First edition, first printing.

444 ———. New York: Modern Library, 1959. First edition, reprint. "First Modern Library Giant Edition."

FAULKNER'S COUNTY

445 *The Best of Faulkner*. Bound page proof for *Faulkner's County*. 490 leaves. pp. 1–490. Brown wrappers, printed label on front.

446 *Faulkner's County*
London: Chatto & Windus, 1955.
[1–14^{16} 15^{12} 16^{16}], 252 ll.
pp. [i–viii] [1–2] 3–494 [495–496].
Green V-cloth; spine stamped in gold and brown. Printed dust jacket.
No new material. Contains "The Bear," "A Rose for Emily," "Barn Burning," "Dry September," "That Evening Sun," "Turnabout," "Shingles for the Lord,"

"A Justice," and "Wash," *As I Lay Dying,* the Nobel Prize address, "Spotted Horses" (from *The Hamlet*), "Percy Grimm" (from *Light in August*), and "The Courthouse" (from *Requiem for a Nun*).

First edition, first printing.

FAULKNER'S UNIVERSITY PIECES

See 768 under Section III, "Verse."

FOUR STORIES

447 *Four Stories.* Selected and edited, with introduction by Otto Neugebauer. Paderborn, Germ.: Ferdinand Schöningh, n.d. Contains, in English, "Death Drag," "Pennsylvania Station," "Barn Burning," and "That Evening Sun."

GO DOWN, MOSES

448 *Go Down, Moses, and Other Stories*
New York: Random House, [1942].
[1–24⁸ 25⁴], 196 ll., 1 insert.
pp. [i–viii] [1–2] 3–383 [384]. 25 cm.
Red V-cloth, front and back covered with salmon paper; spine gold-stamped. Top edge gold. Sheets bulk 1 47/128″ compressed.
Certificate of limitation: ". . . limited to one hundred copies, signed by the author Number [12]," tipped in facing p. [ii].
On copyright page: "First Printing."
The trade and limited copies are from the same printing.
"Was" appears for the first time. "The Fire and the Hearth," "Pantaloon in Black," "The Old People," "The Bear," "Delta Autumn," and "Go Down, Moses" had previous publication.
First edition, first printing.

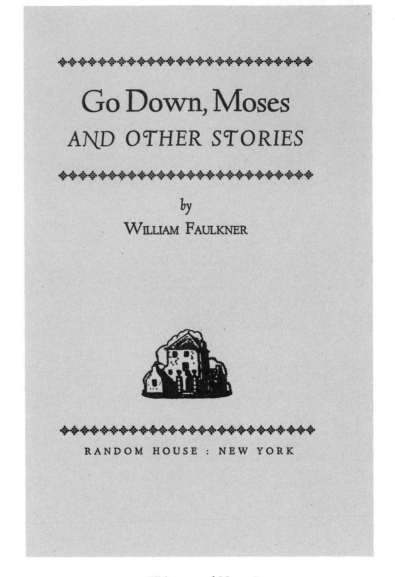

Title page of No. 448

449 ——. New York: Random House, [1942].
[1–24⁸ 25⁴], 196 ll.
pp. [i–viii] [1–2] 3–383 [384].
The trade copies appear in various bindings and on various paper stocks. Ordinarily, difference in bulk is taken as evidence of reimpression; but since unusual methods were employed because of wartime paper shortages, it is likely that in this case the different papers

signify only that make-ready adjustments were made during the run of a single printing.

On copyright page: "First printing."

Copy 1: Maroon V-cloth; spine green-stamped; sheets bulk 1 50/128″ compressed. This and other copies listed have printed dust jackets. Copy 2: Blue T-cloth; spine green-stamped; sheets bulk 1 50/128″ compressed. Copy 3: Maroon H-cloth; spine green-stamped; sheets bulk 1 48/128″ compressed. Copy 4: Light red V-cloth; spine green-stamped; sheets bulk 1 56/128″ compressed. Copy 5: Black V-cloth; spine and front stamped in red and gold; top edge red; sheets bulk 1 48/128″ compressed. Copy 6: Apparent duplicate of Copy 5. Copy 7: Light blue V-cloth; spine green-stamped. Lacks title and signature on front cover.

First edition, first printing.

450 *Go Down, Moses.* New York: Random House, [ca. 1948]. "And Other Stories" has been removed from the title page. First edition, "Second printing."

451 ——. [ca. 1948]. First edition, "Third printing."

452 ——. New York: Modern Library, 1955. First edition, reprint. "First Modern Library Edition."

453 ——. [ca. 1955]. First edition, reprint.

Illustrations of MSS, Typescripts, Etc.

Reproduction of typescript of p. 1 of "Apotheosis." ("Apotheosis" is the penciled-in title of a typescript of "An Absolution," which is apparently an incomplete version of "The Fire on the Hearth," which is an early version of "The Fire and the Hearth.") See 2768 and 2766 Meriwether, "Career" and *Career*.

BRITISH EDITIONS

454 *Go Down, Moses, and Other Stories*
London: Chatto & Windus, 1942.
[A]⁸ B–R⁸, 136 ll.
pp. [1–6] 7–268 [269–272].

Laid paper. Green V-cloth; spine white-stamped. Printed dust jacket.

First British edition, first printing.

455 ——. London: Chatto & Windus, 1960. First British edition, reprint.

456 ——. Harmondsworth: Penguin, 1960. Second British edition, first printing.

TRANSLATIONS

French

457 *Descende, Moïse.* Paris: Gallimard, 1955. Trans. R.-N. Raimbault. Copy 1: Number 53 of 76 on "vélin pur fil Lafuma-Navarre." Copy 2.

German

458 *Das verworfene Erbe.* Stuttgart–Hamburg: Scherz & Goverts, 1953. Trans. with a foreword by Hermann Stresau

459 ——. Zurich: Fretz & Wasmuth, 1953. Separate printing of the Stresau translation.

Italian

460 *Scendi, Mose.* Milan: Mondadori, 1947. Trans. Edoardo Bizzarri. "1 Edizione."

See 1007 *Tutte le opere di William Faulkner*, Vol. II, 1960. The Bizzarri translation.

Spanish

461 *¡Desciende Moises!* Barcelona: Caralt, 1955. Trans. with a foreword by Ana-María de Foronda. "Primera edición."

462 ———. 1955. New edition of the de Foronda translation.

See 1009 *Obras escogidas*, Vol. I, 1956, and 1008 *Obras completas*, Vol. I, 1959. The Caballero Robredo translation in both.

JEALOUSY AND EPISODE

463 *Jealousy and Episode: Two Stories by William Faulkner*. Minneapolis: Faulkner Studies, 1955. Copy 204 of 500. Previously published in the New Orleans *Times-Picayune*, *Faulkner Studies*, III, and the Toyko *New Orleans Sketches*.

KNIGHT'S GAMBIT

464 *Knight's Gambit*
   New York: Random House, [1949].
   The initials "K" and "G," the publisher's emblem, and the curved line are in red; the rest of the title page is printed in black.
   [1–8¹⁶], 128 ll.
   pp. [i–viii] [1–2] 3–246 [247–248]. 20.3 cm.
   Red V-cloth; front and spine stamped in gold and black. Top edge blue. Printed dust jacket.
   Contains, in addition to the title story, which appears for the first time, "Smoke," "Monk," "Hand upon the Waters," "Tomorrow," and "An Error in Chemistry."
   Two copies.
   First edition, first printing.

465 ———. New York: Random House, [ca. 1949]. First edition, "Second printing."

466 ———. New York: New American Library, 1950. Second American edition, "First printing."

467 ———. 1956. Third American edition, probably first printing but designated "Third printing."

WILLIAM FAULKNER

Knight's Gambit

RANDOM HOUSE   NEW YORK

Title page of No. 464

468 ———. *Book Digest*, I, No. 3 (June 1950). An abridgment.

BRITISH EDITIONS

469 *Knight's Gambit*
   London: Chatto & Windus, 1951.
   [1]⁸ 2–14⁸, 112 ll. *Note:* Front and rear endpapers (pastedown and free) are integral.
   pp. [i–ii] [1–8] 9–218 [219–222].

Blue V-cloth; spine gold-stamped. Top edge gray. Printed dust jacket.

First British edition, first printing.

TRANSLATIONS

French

470 *Le gambit du cavalier*. Paris: Gallimard, 1951. Trans. André du Bouchet. Copy 1: Number 29 of 129 on "vélin pur fil des Papeteries Lafuma-Navarre." Copy 2.

German

471 *Der Springer greift an: Erzählungen*. Stuttgart: Goverts, 1960. Trans. Elisabeth Schnack.

472 ——. Zurich: Fretz & Wasmuth, 1962. The Schnack translation.

Italian

See 1007 *Tutte le opere di William Faulkner*, Vol. VI, 1963.

Spanish

473 *Gambito de caballo*. Buenos Aires: Emecé, 1951. Trans. Lucrecia Moreno de Sáenz.

474 ——. [1964]. "Tercera edición."

Miscellaneous

475 *Kishi no otoshiana*. Tokyo: Ondori-sha, 1951. Trans. Yasuo Ōkubo.

476 *Høje ret*. Copenhagen: Wangel, 1952. Trans. Georg Gjedde.

477 *Duman*. Istanbul: Varlik Yayinevi, 1952. Trans. Talât Halman. Contains "Smoke," "Hand upon the Waters," "Tomorrow," "An Error in Chemistry," and "Monk."

478 *Dukhān wa Qisas Ukhrā*. Beirut: Dar al-Kitab, 1957. Trans. with preface by 'Ādil Hāmid. Contains "Smoke," "Idiot," "Hand upon the Waters," "Tomorrow," and "An Error in Chemistry."

479 *Gambit*. Warsaw: Państwowy Instytut Wydawniczy, [1964]. Trans. Zofia Kierszys.

MIRRORS OF CHARTRES STREET

480 *Mirrors of Chartres Street*
Minneapolis: Faulkner Studies, [1953].
[1–7⁸], 56 ll.
pp. [i–vi] vii [viii] ix–xv[xvi] 1–93 [94–96]. 21 cm.
Beige V-cloth; spine stamped in red.
Certificate of limitation: "This is number —— of an edition of one thousand copies."
Copy 1: Number 149, in printed dust jacket. Copy 2: Number 59, no dust jacket. Copy 3: With holograph notation on certificate of limitation: "This is No. 4 of thirteen copies of a press overrun bound by Allan Campbell Minneapolis Sept 1957"; gray V-cloth, spine stamped in red and black.
Reprints eleven prose sketches originally published in the New Orleans *Times-Picayune* in 1925: "Mirrors of Chartres Street," "Damon and Pythias Unlimited," "Home," "Cheest!," "Out of Nazareth," "The Kingdom of God," "The Rosary," "The Cobbler," "Chance," "Sunset," and "The Kid Learns."
First edition, only printing.

NEW ORLEANS SKETCHES

481 *New Orleans Sketches*
Ed. Ichiro Nishizaki. In English.
Tokyo: Hokuseido, 1955.

Title page of No. 480

[1–8⁸ 9⁴], 68 ll., 1 insert.
pp. [4] [i] ii [iii–iv] 7–134 (= 136).
Blue V-cloth; spine gold-stamped. Printed dust jacket.
Photograph of Faulkner tipped in facing title page, and Japanese colophon pasted on free rear endpaper.
Reprints thirteen prose sketches originally published in the New Orleans *Times-Picayune* in 1925. Eleven

are reprinted from *Mirrors of Chartres Street*, and two, "Episode" and "Jealousy," are reprinted from *Faulkner Studies*, III (Winter 1954).
First edition.

482 ——. Tokyo: Hokuseido, 1957.

483 ——. 1958.

484 ——. Ed. Carvel Collins.
New Brunswick: Rutgers University Press, 1958.
[1–7¹⁶], 112 ll.
pp. [1–8] 9–223 [224].
Brown boards with gold-stamped maroon V-cloth shelfback. Beige endpapers. Printed dust jacket.
In addition to the thirteen sketches previously reprinted in the Japanese *New Orleans Sketches*, this volume contains three other sketches from the New Orleans *Times-Picayune:* "The Liar," "Country Mice," and "Yo Ho and Two Bottles of Rum." Also included is "New Orleans," a group of eleven sketches from the *Double Dealer*, VII, No. 41–42 (January–February 1925).
The text of this volume is reliable.
First American edition, "First printing."

485 ——. New York: Grove, 1961. First American edition, reprint.

BRITISH EDITIONS

486 *New Orleans Sketches.* Ed. Carvel Collins.
London: Sidgwick & Jackson, 1959. First American edition, British reprint.

487 ——. London: Brown, Watson, [ca. 1961]. New edition.

TRANSLATIONS—COMPLETE AND SELECTED

German

488 *New Orleans: Skizzen und Erzählungen.*
Stuttgart: Goverts, 1962. Trans. Arno Schmidt.

489 ——. Zurich: Fretz & Wasmuth, [1962]. The Schmidt translation.

Italian

490 *New Orleans.* Milan: Il Saggiatore, 1959. Trans. Cesare Salmaggi. "Prima edizione." Contains "The Kingdom of God," "Out of Nazareth," "The Kid Learns," "The Liar," "Country Mice," and "Yo Ho and Two Bottles of Rum."

Spanish

491 *Historias de Nueva Orleans.* Barcelona: Caralt, [1964]. Trans. Francisco Elias.

NOVELLER

492 *Noveller.* Oslo: Gyldendal, 1951. Trans. with foreword by Leo Strøm. Contains fourteen stories: "Was," "Barn Burning," "Two Soldiers," "Dry September," "All the Dead Pilots," "That Evening Sun," "Red Leaves," "A Justice," "A Courtship," "Ad Astra," "Wash," "Honor," "Doctor Martino," and "Carcassonne."

DE OUDE MAN/DE BEER

493 *De oude Man/De Beer.* Hasselt, Belg.: Uitgeverij Heideland, 1962. Trans. with introduction by John Vandenbergh. Contains "The Old Man," "The Hound," "A Rose for Emily," "A Courtship," "The Bear," and "The Fire and the Hearth."

THE PORTABLE FAULKNER

494 *The Portable Faulkner.* Ed. Malcolm Cowley. New York: Viking, 1946. First appearance of Faulkner's "Appendix: 1699, 1945. The Compsons," of the map of Yoknapatawpha on the endpapers, and of Cowley's introduction (for reprints and reviews of which see 516, 529, 1346, 1644, 1646, and 2417–2420). Contains also "A Justice," "Red Leaves," "Was," "Wash," "The Bear," "That Evening Sun," "Ad Astra," "A Rose for Emily," "Death Drag," "Delta Autumn," *Old Man*, "Wedding in the Rain" (from *Absalom, Absalom!*), "Raid" (from *The Unvanquished*), "Spotted Horses" (from *The Hamlet*), "Dilsey" (from *The Sound and the Fury*), "Uncle Bud and the Three Madams" (from *Sanctuary*), and "Percy Grimm" (from *Light in August*). First edition, first printing.

495 ——. 1949. First edition, "SECOND PRINTING."

496 *The Indispensable Faulkner.* New York: Book Society, 1950. Same contents as *The Portable Faulkner.* First edition, reprint.

497 *The Portable Faulkner.* New York: Viking, 1961. First edition, "SEVENTH PRINTING (X P)."

TRANSLATIONS—ITALIAN

498 *664 pagine di William Faulkner.* Milan: Il Saggiatore, 1959. Trans. Edoardo Bizzarri *et al.* A translation of *The Portable Faulkner* plus excerpts from *Requiem for a Nun:* "Il tribunale (Un nome per la città)" and "La prigione (Neanche allora proprio rinunciare)."

A ROSE FOR EMILY

499 *A Rose for Emily.* Ed. Naotarō Takiguchi and Masaō Takahashi. Tokyo: Nan'un-do, 1956. In English; contains, in addition to the title story, "Shall Not Perish," "That Evening Sun," and "Crevasse."

A ROSE FOR EMILY AND OTHER STORIES

500   *A Rose for Emily and Other Stories*
New York: Editions for the Armed Services, [1945].
128 ll.
pp. [1–4] 5–255 [256].   9.8 x 14.3 cm.
Printed wrappers.
Eight stories, all previously published: "A Rose for Emily," "The Hound," "Turn About," "That Evening Sun," "Dry September," "Delta Autumn," "Barn Burning," and "An Odor of Verbena."

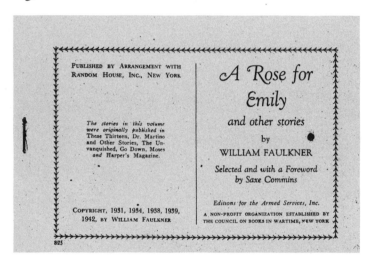

Title page of No. 500

TRANSLATIONS—MISCELLANEOUS

501   *Emily no bara*.   Tokyo: Cosmopolitan-sha, 1952. Trans. Naotarō Takiguchi.

SELECTED SHORT STORIES OF WILLIAM FAULKNER

502   *Selected Short Stories of William Faulkner*.   New York: Modern Library, 1962.   Contains thirteen stories: "Barn Burning," "Two Soldiers," "A Rose for Emily,"

"Dry September," "That Evening Sun," "Red Leaves," "Lo!," "Turnabout [*sic*]," "Honor," "There Was a Queen," "Mountain Victory," "Beyond," and "Race at Morning."   First edition, "First printing."

SEM' RASSKAZOV

503   *Sem' rasskazov* [Seven Stories].   Moscow: Izdatel'stvo inostrannoi literatury, 1958.   Trans. with afterword by I. Kashkin *et al.*   Contains "Barn Burning," "A Justice," "Red Leaves," "That Evening Sun," "Smoke," "Percy Grimm" (from *Light in August*), and "Victory."

SMÁSÖGUR

504   *Smásögur*.   Reykjavik: Almenna Bókafélagid, 1956.   Trans. Kristján Karlsson.   With a foreword and six stories: "Dry September," "Elly," "That Evening Sun," "Wash," "A Rose for Emily," and "A Justice."

THE TALL MEN AND OTHER STORIES

505   [*The Tall Men and Other Stories.*]   Ed., in English, with notes in Japanese by Kenzo Sakai.   Kyoto: Muse Library (Apollon-sha), n.d.

THESE 13

506   *These 13*
New York: Jonathan Cape and Harrison Smith, [1931].

Title page of No. 506

Frame and cut on title page in red, the rest in black.
[1⁸(1₂ + 1) 2–23⁸], 185 ll.
pp. [i–xii] [1–2] 3–358.   21 cm.
Laid paper.   Silver-flecked tan B-cloth covers; coarse-grained red-brown cloth shelfback.   Top edge silver.   Gray endpapers.
Certificate of limitation: "Of this special edition 299

copies (of which 289 are for sale) were printed for Jonathan Cape and Harrison Smith in August, 1931. Each copy is signed by the author.   This copy is number 240," p. [vi].

The table of contents reads "280" for "208."   The folios are in italic type enclosed in brackets:

The trade and limited copies of this book are separate printings, but priority has not been established.

First appearance of "Victory," "All the Dead Pilots," "Crevasse," "A Justice," "Mistral," "Divorce in Naples," and "Carcassone."   "Ad Astra," "Red Leaves," "A Rose for Emily," "Hair," "That Evening Sun," and "Dry September" had previous publication.

First edition, presumably first printing.

507 ——.   New York: Jonathan Cape and Harrison Smith, [1931].

The title page is printed in black.
[1–23⁸], 184 ll.
pp. i–x [1–2] 3–358.
Wove paper.   Blue V-cloth covers; red-stamped gray V-cloth shelfback.   Top edge black.   Blue and white endpapers.

On copyright page: "First published, 1931."
Table of contents uncorrected.
The folios are in roman type without brackets.

Three copies in printed dust jackets.   Copy 1: Inscribed on half-title, "For Alice and Harold, from Bill," and also inscribed on title page, "William Faulkner Oxford, Miss. For Alice and Harold Guinzberg."   Copy 2: Signed on title page, "William Faulkner."   Copy 3.

First edition, presumably second printing.

508 ——.   New York: Cape & Smith, 1931.   Table of contents corrected.   First edition, "Second Printing, September, 1931," actually the third printing.

509 ——.   1931.   First edition, "Third Printing, October, 1931," actually the fourth printing.

BRITISH EDITIONS

510 *These Thirteen*
London: Chatto & Windus, 1933.
[A]⁸ B–Z⁸, 184 ll., 2 inserts.

pp. [i–viii] [1–2] 3–357 [358–360].
Blue V-cloth, spine gold-stamped. Top edge green.
Two leaves of advertisements inserted facing p. [358].
Copy 1: Printed dust jacket. Copy 2.
First edition, first British reprint.

TRANSLATIONS

French

511 *Treize histoires.* Paris: Gallimard, 1939. Trans. R.-N. Raimbault, Ch.-P. Vorce, and M.-E. Coindreau. Preface by Raimbault. Number 54 of 20 copies numbered 51–70, "hors commerce" on "alfa des Papeteries Lafuma Navarre."

Italian

512 *Questi tredici.* Turin: Lattes, 1948. Trans. with preface by Francesco Lo Bue.

Spanish

513 *Estos trece.* Buenos Aires: Losada, 1956. Trans. Aurora Bernárdez.

Miscellaneous—Selected

514 *Victorie.* Bucharest: Editura de stat pentru literatura si arta, [ca. 1957]. Trans. Margareta Sterian.

SINGLE STORIES

517 "Ad Astra." *American Caravan IV*, ed. Alfred Kreymborg, Lewis Mumford, and Paul Rosenfeld. New York: Macaulay, 1931. Copy 1: Number 89 of 250. Copy 2.

Contains "Victory," "Dry September," "A Rose for Emily," "Red Leaves," and "A Justice."

THREE FAMOUS NOVELS

515 *Three Famous Novels.* New York: Random House, 1958. Contains "Spotted Horses," *Old Man*, and "The Bear."

TWELVE AMERICAN WRITERS

516 *Twelve American Writers.* Ed. William M. Gibson and George Arms. New York: Macmillan, 1962. Contains "The Kingdom of God," "A Louisiana Sheep-Ranch" (excerpt from *Mosquitoes*), "Dry September," "That Evening Sun," "Carcassonne," "Barn Burning," "The Bear," "Shingles for the Lord," as well as the Nobel Prize address, "Sherwood Anderson, An Appreciation," "Interview in New York in Early 1956" (an excerpt from the Stein interview as published in 895 *Writers at Work*, 1958), Jean-Paul Sartre, "American Novelists in French Eyes," 1946, and Robert Penn Warren, "William Faulkner," 1946.

WILLIAM FAULKNER: EARLY PROSE AND POETRY

See 770 and related entries under Section III, "Verse."

518 "Afternoon of a Cow by Ernest V. Trueblood." *Furioso*, II, No. 4 (Summer 1947). "Notes on Mr. Faulkner" by R[eed] W[hitemore].

TRANSLATIONS—FRENCH

519 "L'après-midi d'une vache par Ernest V. Trueblood." *Fontaine*, No. 27–28 (June–July 1943). Trans. with note by Maurice-Edgar Coindreau.

520 ——. *Écrivains américains d'aujourd'hui.* Geneva: Continent, 1944. The Coindreau translation.

521 ——. *Écrivains et poètes des États-Unis.* Paris: Fontaine, 1945. The Coindreau translation and note.

522 "All the Dead Pilots." *The Short Story*, ed. James B. Hall and Joseph Langland. New York: Macmillan, 1956. With commentary.

523 "Ambuscade." *Saturday Evening Post*, CCVII, No. 13 (September 29, 1934).

OTHER PRINTINGS

524 "Ambuscade." *The Post Reader of Civil War Stories*, ed. Gordon Carroll. New York: Doubleday, 1958. Contains also "A Mountain Victory."

525 "Artist at Home." *Story*, III, No. 14 (August 1933).

OTHER PRINTINGS

526 "Artist at Home." *Story in America, 1933–1934*, ed. Whit Burnett and Martha Foley. New York: Vanguard Press, 1934.

527 "Barn Burning." *Harper's Magazine*, No. 1069 (June 1939). Two copies.

OTHER PRINTINGS

528 "Barn Burning." *O. Henry Memorial Award Prize Stories of 1939*, ed. Harry Hansen. New York: Doubleday, Doran, 1939.

529 ——. *College Reading*, ed. George Sanderlin. Boston: Heath, 1953. Contains also Malcolm Cowley's introduction to *The Portable Faulkner* and Faulkner's Nobel Prize address.

530 ——. *Short Story Masterpieces*, ed. Robert Penn Warren and Albert Erskine. New York: Dell, 1954.

531 ——. *A Southern Reader*, ed. Willard Thorp. New York: Knopf, 1955.

532 ——. *First-Prize Stories 1919–1960*, ed. Harry Hansen. Garden City: Hanover House, 1960. Contains also "A Courtship."

Illustrations of MSS, Typescripts, Etc.

Reproduction of first MS page. See 2768 and 2766 Meriwether, "Career" and *Career*.

DRAMATIC ADAPTATIONS

533 "Barn Burning." Gore Vidal. *Visit to a Small Planet and Other Television Plays*. Boston: Little, Brown, 1957. Contains also an adaptation of "Smoke."

TRANSLATIONS—FRENCH

534 "L'incendiaire." *L'Âge nouveau*, No. 74–76 (June–August 1952). Trans. R.-N. Raimbault.

535 "The Bear." *Saturday Evening Post*, CCXIV, No. 45 (May 9, 1942). Revision of "A Bear Hunt."

OTHER PRINTINGS

536 "The Bear." *Masters of the Modern Short Story*, ed. Walter Havighurst. New York: Harcourt, Brace, 1945.

537 ——. *The College Omnibus*, ed. Leonard F. Dean. 7th ed. New York: Harcourt, Brace, 1951. With study notes.

538 ——. *Great Short Stories*, ed. Wilbur Schramm. New York: Harcourt, Brace, 1952.

539 ——. *Nine Short Novels*, ed. Richard M. Ludwig and Marvin B. Perry, Jr. Boston: Heath, 1952.

540 ——. *The Creative Reader*, ed. R. W. Stallman and R. E. Watters. New York: Ronald Press, [1954].

541 ——. *Six Great Modern Short Novels*. New York: Dell, 1956.

542 ——. Paderborn, Germ.: Ferdinand Schöningh, 1958. Abridged, with notes in German by Dr. Alex Niederstenbruch. Two copies.

543 ——. Tokyo: Kaibunsha, 1963. Ed. with notes in Japanese by Shuichi Motoda.

544 ——. *Bear, Man, and God: Seven Approaches to William Faulkner's* The Bear, ed. Francis Lee Utley *et al*. New York: Random House, 1964. Contains the text of "The Bear" from *Go Down, Moses and Other Stories* and the *Saturday Evening Post* version. Also contains the following other works by Faulkner: "Sam Fathers," "Delta Autumn," "Lion," "Race at Morning," "The Blood Ritual of Isaac McCaslin," "Boon Hogganbeck," "Was" (an excerpt), *The Hamlet* (an excerpt), and the Nobel Prize address.

545 ——. *American Literature*, ed. Geoffrey Moore. London: Faber and Faber, [1964]. Uncorrected proof copy in wrappers. Contains "The Bear," with introductory note by the editor, pp. 1131–1213.

Excerpts

546 "An Insignificant Fyce Baits a Bear." *Life*, XXXIX, No. 20 (November 14, 1955).

TRANSLATIONS

German

547 *Der Bär*. Frankfurt–Vienna: Forum, [1958?]. Trans. Hermann Stresau.

548 ——. Berlin–Frankfurt: Suhrkamp, 1960. The Stresau translation. "Erstes bis fünftes Tausend."

Miscellaneous

549 "O urso." *Mestres do moderno conto americano*. Lisbon: Portugália, [1950?]. Trans. Gabral do Nascimento.

550 *Medved*. Novi Sad: Matica srpska, 1954. Trans. into Serbian by Aleksandar Nejgebauer. Three copies.

551 *Bjørnen*. Copenhagen: Gyldendal, 1957. Trans. with preface by Ole Storm.

552 *Björnen*. Stockholm: Rabén & Sjorgren, 1959. Trans. with introduction by Olov Jonason. Contains a genealogy of the McCaslin-Edmonds-Beauchamp groups, from *Faulkner Studies*, I (1952).

553 ——. Stockholm: Aldus/Bonniers, [1964]. The Jonason translation with genealogy.

554 *A medve*. Budapest: Európa Könyvkiadó, [1960?]. Trans. into Hungarian by Viktor Janos.

555 [*The Bear.*] Rangoon: Shumawa, 1961. In Burmese.

556 "A Bear Hunt." *Saturday Evening Post*, CCVI, No. 33 (February 10, 1934).

557 "Beyond." *Harper's Magazine*, No. 1000 (September 1933).

OTHER PRINTINGS

558 "Beyond." *The Best Short Stories of 1934 and The Yearbook of the American Short Story*, ed. Edward J. O'Brien. Boston–New York: Houghton Mifflin, 1934.

TRANSLATIONS—FRENCH

559 "Au-delà." *Fontaine*, IX, No. 52 (May 1946). Trans. R.-N. Raimbault.

560 "The Brooch." *Scribner's Magazine*, XCIX, No. 1 (January 1936).

TRANSLATIONS—FRENCH

561 "La broche." *Figaro littéraire*, July 14, 1962. Trans. R.-N. Raimbault. Two portraits.

562 "By the People." *Mademoiselle*, XLI, No. 41 (October 1955).

OTHER PRINTINGS

563 "By the People." *Prize Stories 1957—The O. Henry Awards*, ed. Paul Engle and Constance Urdang. Garden City: Doubleday, 1957. Also galley proof.

564 ——. *40 Best Stories from Mademoiselle, 1935–1960*, ed. Cyrilly Abels and Margarita G. Smith. New York: Harper, 1960.

See also 139 *The Mansion*, 1959.

Illustrations of MSS, Typescripts, Etc.

Reproduction of typescript p. 5 with authorial revisions. See 2766 Meriwether, *Career.*

565 "Carcassonne." *Dude*, I, No. 4 (March 1957).

TRANSLATIONS—MISCELLANEOUS

566 "Carcassonne." *Yenilik* (Istanbul), IX, No. 44 (August 1956). Trans. Bilge Barasu.

567 "Centaur in Brass." *American Mercury*, XXV, No. 98 (February 1932).

TRANSLATIONS—FRENCH

568 "Le centaure de bronze." *Œuvres libres*, No. 182 (June 25, 1961). Trans. R.-N. Raimbault.

569 "A Courtship." *Sewanee Review*, LVI, No. 4 (Autumn 1948).

OTHER PRINTINGS

570 "A Courtship." *Prize Stories of 1949: The O. Henry Awards*, ed. Herschel Brickell. Garden City: Doubleday, 1949.

See also 532 *First-Prize Stories 1919–1960*, ed. Harry Hansen, 1960.

571 "Death-Drag." *Scribner's Magazine*, XCI, No. 1 (January 1932). Two copies.

572 "Delta Autumn." *Story*, XX, No. 95 (May–June 1942).

OTHER PRINTINGS

573 "Delta Autumn." *The Story Pocket Book*, ed. Whit Burnett. New York: Pocket Books, [1944]. "First Printing December, 1944."

574 ——. 1945.

575 ——. *Short Stories in Context*, ed. Woodburn O. Ross and A. Dayle Wallace. New York: American Book Co., 1953.

576 ——. *A New Southern Harvest*, ed. Robert Penn Warren and Albert Erskine. New York: Bantam, 1957.

577 "Divorce in Naples." *The Gent*, I, No. 5 (June 1957).

578 "Doctor Martino." *Harper's Magazine*, No. 978 (November 1931). Two copies.

579 "Dry September." *Scribner's Magazine*, LXXXIX, No. 1 (January 1931).

OTHER PRINTINGS

580 "Dry September." *Reader and Writer*, ed. Harrison Hayford and Howard P. Vincent. 2d ed. Boston: Houghton Mifflin, 1954.

581 ——. *Ten Modern Masters*, ed. Robert Gorham Davis. 2d ed. New York: Harcourt, Brace, 1959. Contains also "The Old People" and "Shingles for the Lord."

582 ——. *American Short Stories*, ed. Douglas Grant. New York: Oxford University Press, 1965.

583 "Elly." *Story*, IV, No. 19 (February 1934).

TRANSLATIONS—FRENCH

584 "Elly." *Fontaine*, VII, No. 36 (1944). Trans. Hélène Bokanowski.

585 "Episode." Faulkner Studies, III (Winter 1954).

TRANSLATIONS—MISCELLANEOUS

586 "Episod." *All världens berättare* (Stockholm), No. 11 (November 1955). Trans. Brita Eijde.

587 "An Error in Chemistry." *Ellery Queen's Mystery Magazine*, VII, No. 31 (June 1946).

OTHER PRINTINGS

588 "An Error in Chemistry." *The Queen's Awards, 1946*, ed. Ellery Queen (*pseud.*). Boston: Little, Brown, 1946.

589 ——. *Best Crime Stories*, ed. John Welcome. London: Faber and Faber, [1964].

590 "Fool about a Horse." *Scribner's Magazine*, C, No. 2 (August 1936).

OTHER PRINTINGS

591 "Fool about a Horse." *The Best Short Stories 1937 and The Yearbook of the American Short Story*, ed. Edward J. O'Brien. Boston–New York: Houghton Mifflin, 1937.

Illustrations of MSS, Typescripts, Etc.

Reproduction of first MS page and typescript p. 23. See 2768 and 2766 Meriwether, "Career" and *Career*.

592 "Fox Hunt." *Harper's Magazine*, No. 976 (September 1931). Two copies.

OTHER PRINTINGS

593 "Fox Hunt." *The PL Book of Modern American Short Stories*, ed. Nicholas Moore. London: Editions Poetry London, 1945.

TRANSLATIONS—FRENCH

594 "Chasse au renard." *Courtes histoires américaines*. Paris: Corrêa, 1948. Trans. R.-N. Raimbault.

595 "Go Down, Moses." *Collier's*, CVII, No. 4 (January 25, 1941).

OTHER PRINTINGS

596 "Go Down, Moses." *Modern Short Stories*, ed. with introduction and notes by Jim Hunter. London: Faber and Faber, [1964].

TRANSLATIONS—EXCERPTS

597 "O funeral dum negro." *Os melhores contos americanos*, ed. João Gaspar Simões. Lisbon: Portugália, [1943?]. Trans. Tomaz Kim.

598 "İn, Musa, İn . . ." *Yenilik* (Istanbul), VIII (April 1956). Trans. Bilge Karasu.

599 "Gold Is Not Always." *Atlantic Monthly*, CLXVI, No. 5 (November 1940). Two copies.

OTHER PRINTINGS

600 "Gold Is Not Always." *Jubilee: One Hundred Years of the Atlantic*, ed. Edward Weeks and Emily Flint. Boston: Little, Brown, 1957.

601 ——. *New England Oracle*, ed. Edward Weeks and Emily Flint, with introduction by D. W. Brogan. London: Collins, 1958. "A Choice Selection from One Hundred Years of the *Atlantic Monthly*."

TRANSLATIONS—MISCELLANEOUS

602 "Ikke altid guld." *Hele vejen rundt*. Copenhagen: Branners, 1943. Trans. H. C. Branner.

603 "Golden Land." *American Mercury*, XXXV, No. 137 (May 1935). Two copies.

604 "Hair" *American Mercury*, XXIII, No. 89 (May 1931). Two copies.

605 "Hand upon the Waters." *Saturday Evening Post*, CCXII, No. 19 (November 4, 1939).

OTHER PRINTINGS

606 "Hand upon the Waters." *Best Short Stories 1940 and The Yearbook of the American Short Story*, ed. Edward J. O'Brien. Boston: Houghton Mifflin, 1940.

"The Hill." See *768 Faulkner's University Pieces*, ed. Carvel Collins, 1962, and *770 William Faulkner: Early Prose and Poetry*, ed. Carvel Collins, 1962.

607 "Honor." *American Mercury*, XX, No. 79 (July 1930). Two copies.

608 "The Hound." *Harper's Magazine*, No. 975 (August 1931).

OTHER PRINTINGS

609 "The Hound." *The American Literary Record*, ed. Willard Thorp *et al*. Philadelphia: Lippincott, 1961.

610 "Idyll in the Desert." Author's typescript, 19 pp. With holograph revisions.

611 *Idyll in the Desert*
New York: Random House, 1931.
The floral cut is red-brown; the rest of the title page is printed in black.
[1¹²], 12 ll.
pp. [i–ii] [1–3] 4–17 [18–22]. 21.8 cm.
Red marbled boards, printed label on front.
Certificate of limitation: "Of this edition four hundred copies were printed in the week of December 7

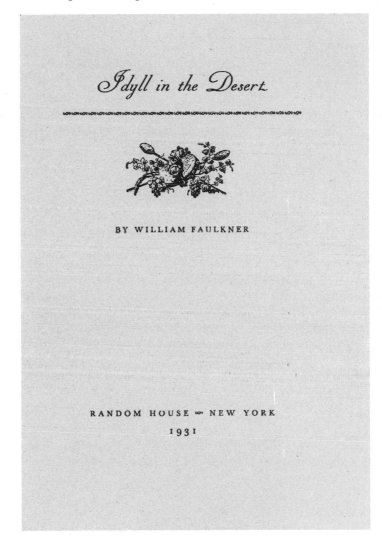

Idyll in the Desert

BY WILLIAM FAULKNER

RANDOM HOUSE ∞ NEW YORK
1931

Title page of No. 611

nineteen hundred and thirty one by The Harbor Press, New York   This copy being number [   ] signed by the author . . . ," p. [18].

On copyright page: "First Edition."

Copy 1: Number 9, in glassine dust jacket, inscribed on free front endpaper, "For Bill Conselman   Faulkner May 26 1932   Los Angeles."   Copy 2: Number 297, in glassine dust jacket.   Copy 3: "Out of series."   Copy 4: Number 387, in glassine dust jacket.

Only edition, only printing.

612   "Jealousy."   *Faulkner Studies*, III (Winter 1954).

613   "The Kid Learns."   *Anthology of Best Short Short Stories*, Volume 7, ed. Robert Oberfirst.   New York: Fell, 1959.

OTHER PRINTINGS

614   "The Kid Learns."   *Gamma 2* (North Hollywood), I, No. 2 (1963), 45–49.   Reprinted from *New Orleans Sketches*.

615   ["Knight's   Gambit."]   *Konjički   gambit*. Belgrade: Prosveta, 1954.   Trans. into Serbian by Božidar Marković.

"Landing   in   Luck."   See 768 *Faulkner's University Pieces*, ed. Carvel Collins, 1962, and 770 *William Faulkner: Early Prose and Poetry*, ed. Carvel Collins, 1962.

616   "Lion."   *Harper's Magazine*, No. 1027 (December 1935).

OTHER PRINTINGS

617   "Lion."   *O. Henry Memorial Award Prize Stories of 1936*, ed. Harry Hansen.   Garden City: Doubleday, Doran, 1936.

618   "Lizards   in   Jamshyd's   Courtyard."   *Saturday Evening Post*, CCIV, No. 35 (February 27, 1932).

619   "Lo."   *Story*, V, No. 28 (November 1934).

OTHER PRINTINGS

620   "Lo."   *The Best Short Stories 1935 and The Yearbook of the American Short Story*, ed. Edward J. O'Brien.   Boston–New York: Houghton Mifflin, 1935.

621   *Miss Zilphia Gant*
Dallas: The Book Club of Texas, 1932.
The scissors are in brown; the rest of the title page is printed in black.
[1–3⁸], 24 ll.
pp. [2] [i–vi] vii–xi [xii] 1–29 [30–34].   19.8 cm.
Brown V-cloth, gold-stamped on front and spine.
Certificate of limitation: ". . . published for the first time in an edition of 300 copies for distribution to the members of the Book Club of Texas. . . . No. [   ]," p. [31].

Copy 1: Number 121, signed "William Faulkner" on the half title and with promotional material laid in. Copy 2: Number 298.   Copy 3: Number 94.

Only edition in English, only printing.

TRANSLATIONS—ITALIAN

622   *La pallida Zilphia Gant*.   Milan: Il Saggiatore, 1959.   Trans. with preface by Fernanda Pivano.

623   "Monk."   *Scribner's Magazine*, CL, No. 5 (May 1937).

OTHER PRINTINGS

624   "Monk."   *The Literature of Crime*, ed. Ellery Queen (*pseud.*).   Boston: Little, Brown, 1950.

625   "A Mountain Victory."   *Saturday Evening Post*, CCV, No. 23 (December 3, 1932).

OTHER PRINTINGS

626   "A Mountain Victory."   *The Post Reader of Civil War Stories*, ed. Gordon Carroll.   New York: Doubleday, 1958.   Contains also "Ambuscade."

MISS
ZILPHIA GANT

BY
WILLIAM FAULKNER

THE BOOK CLUB OF TEXAS
1932

Title page of No. 621

TRANSLATIONS—GERMAN

627 *Sieg in den Bergen.* Munich: Langen und Müller, 1956. Trans. with afterword by Hans Hennecke. "1.-5. Tausend." Two copies.

628 "Mule in the Yard." *Scribner's Magazine*, XCVI, No. 2 (August 1934).

Illustrations of MSS, Typescripts, Etc.

Reproduction of MS p. 1. See 2766 Meriwether, *Career.*

629 "My Grandmother Millard and General Bedford Forrest and the Battle of Harrykin Creek." *Story*, XXII, No. 100 (March–April 1943).

OTHER PRINTINGS

630 "My Grandmother Millard and General Bedford Forrest and the Battle of Harrykin Creek." *Story: The Fiction of the Forties*, ed. Whit and Hallie Burnett. New York: Dutton, 1949.

631 ——. *Stories for Here and Now*, ed. Joseph Greene and Elizabeth Abell. New York: Bantam, 1951.

632 ——. *The Night before Chancellorsville*, ed. Shelby Foote. New York: New American Library, 1957.

633 *Notes on a Horsethief*
   Greenville, Miss.: The Levee Press, 1950.
   [1–5^8], 40 ll.
   pp. [i–vi] [1] 2–71 [72–74]. 23.3 cm.
   Green V-cloth, silver-stamped on front and spine. Pale-green endpapers with green line drawings.
   Certificate of limitation: "Of this edition of nine hundred and seventy-five copies . . . nine hundred and fifty copies are for sale. This is copy [   ] signed by the author," p. [73].
   Decorations by Elizabeth Calvert.
   Copy 1: Number 65, with cellophane dust jacket. Copy 2: Number 350.
   First edition, only separate printing.

OTHER PRINTINGS

634 ——. *Vogue* page proof distributed as promotional material. 46–51, 101–104, [105–106].

635 ——. *Vogue*, CXXIV, No. 1 (July 1954).

636 "The Old People." *Harper's Magazine*, No. 1084 (September 1940).

WILLIAM FAULKNER

Notes on a Horsethief

DECORATIONS BY ELIZABETH CALVERT
THE LEVEE PRESS GREENVILLE MISSISSIPPI

1950

Title page of No. 633

OTHER PRINTINGS

637 "The Old People." *O. Henry Memorial Award Prize Stories of 1941*, ed. Herschel Brickell. Garden City: Doubleday, Doran, 1941.

638 ——. New York: Book League of America, 1941. Reprint of preceding.

639 ——. *The Avon All-American Fiction Reader.* New York: Avon, 1951.

640 ——. *The Story*, ed. Mark Schorer. New York: Prentice-Hall, 1953.

——. See 581 *Ten Modern Masters*, ed. Robert Gorham Davis, 1959.

EXCERPTS AND TRANSLATIONS—
MISCELLANEOUS

641 *Het oude Volk*. Delft: Gaade, 1957. Trans. with preface by Hans Edinga.

642 ["The Old People."] *Ameryka*, No. 3 (March 1959). Excerpt in Polish. Includes an article by Nathan Glick entitled "Kierunki w nowoczesnej Powieści amerykańskiej" (Trends in the Modern American Novel) with comments on Faulkner. Mimeographed text of the Glick article in English laid in.

643 "Once aboard the lugger." *Contempo*, I, No. 17 (February 1, 1932). Two copies, one of which has been autographed on the front page by Faulkner.

644 "Pantaloon in Black." *Harper's Magazine*, No. 1085 (October 1940). Two copies.

645 "Pennsylvania Station." *American Mercury*, XXXI, No. 122 (February 1934). Three copies.

TRANSLATIONS—GERMAN

646 "Pennsylvania Station." *Amerika erzählt*, ed. Heinz Politzer. Frankfurt–Hamburg: Fischer, 1958. Trans. Kurt Heinrich Hansen.

647 "A Point of Law." *Collier's*, CV, No. 25 (June 22, 1940).

648 "A Portrait of Elmer." Author's typescript, 57 p., with two holograph corrections. Unpublished, complete version.

649 "Race at Morning." *Saturday Evening Post,* CCXXVII, No. 36 (March 5, 1955).

OTHER PRINTINGS

650 "Race at Morning." *Saturday Evening Post Stories 1955.* New York: Random House, 1955.

651 ——. *Prize Stories 1956: The O. Henry Awards,* ed. Paul Engle and Hansford Martin. Garden City: Doubleday, 1956.

652 ——. *Reading for Pleasure,* ed. Bennett Cerf. New York: Harper, 1957.

TRANSLATIONS—FRENCH

653 "Chasse matinale." *Les vingt meilleures nouvelles américaines,* ed. Alain Bosquet. Paris: Seghers, 1957. Trans. R.-N. Raimbault.

654 "Raid." *Saturday Evening Post,* CCVII, No. 18 (November 3, 1934).

655 "Red Leaves." *Saturday Evening Post,* CCIII, No. 17 (October 25, 1930).

OTHER PRINTINGS

656 "Red Leaves." *Types of Prose Fiction,* ed. George P. Elliott. New York: Random House, [1964].

TRANSLATIONS—MISCELLANEOUS

657 "Folhas vermelhas." *Perspectivas dos Estados Unidos.* Lisbon: Portugália, [1958?]. Trans. Jorge de Sena. Two copies.

658 "Retreat." *Saturday Evening Post,* CCVII, No. 15 (October 13, 1934).

659 "A Rose for Emily." *Forum,* LXXXIII, No. 4 (April 1930).

OTHER PRINTINGS

660 "A Rose for Emily." *Modern Tales of Horror,* ed. Dashiell Hammett. London: Gollancz, 1932.

661 ——. *Creeps by Night,* selected by Dashiell Hammett. New York: Blue Ribbon Books, [1936]. American edition of preceding.

662 ——. *American Harvest,* ed. Allen Tate and John Peale Bishop. New York: Fischer, 1942.

663 ——. *Understanding Fiction,* ed. Cleanth Brooks and Robert Penn Warren. New York: Appleton-Century-Crofts, 1943.

664 ——. *The Bedside Tales.* New York: Editions for the Armed Services, [ca. 1945]. Introduction by Peter Arno.

665 ——. *The Art of Modern Fiction,* ed. Ray B. West, Jr., and Robert Wooster Stallman. New York: Rinehart, 1949.

666 ——. Alternate ed. With *Teacher's Manual.*

667 ——. *American Short Stories,* ed. Dr. Theodor Wolpers. Paderborn, Germ.: Ferdinand Schöningh, n.d. With introductory remarks, biographical notes, and annotations.

668 ——. *History and Anthology of American Literature,* ed. Leighton B. Brown and Takashi Kawatsu. Tokyo: Hokuseido, 1952.

669 ——. *Modern American Short Stories* (Second Series), ed. with notes by Masami Nishikawa. Tokyo: Kenkyusha, [1958].

TRANSLATIONS

French

670 "Une rose pour Emily." *Commerce,* XXIX (Winter 1932). Trans M.-E. Coindreau. Number 431 of 2900 "exemplaires sur alfa."

Miscellaneous

671 "Emily için bir gül." *Varlik* (Istanbul), I, sayi 367 (February 1951). Trans. Orhan Azizoğlu.

672 "En rose til Emily." *Alverdens fortællere*, ed. Sigurd Hoel. Copenhagen: Hasselbalch, 1952. Trans. Jens Kruuse.

673 "Ena rodo gea tia Amilia." *Amerikanika diegemata*. Athens: Ikarus, 1953. Trans. K. Papapágou.

674 "Kwiaty dla Emilii." *Opowieści z dreszczykiem*, ed. Wojciech Zukrowski and Tadeusz Adrian Malanowski. Warsaw: Państwowy Instytut Wydawniczy, 1957. Trans. Malanowski.

675 "Uma rosa para Emily." *Contos norteamericanos*. Rio de Janeiro: Biblioteca Universal Popular, 1963. Trans. Lia Corrêa Dutra.

676 "Shall Not Perish." *Story*, XXIII, No. 102 (July–August 1943).

677 "Shingles for the Lord." *Saturday Evening Post*, CCXV, No. 33 (February 13, 1943).

OTHER PRINTINGS

"Shingles for the Lord." See 581 *Ten Modern Masters*, ed. Robert Gorham Davis, 1959.

678 "Skirmish at Sartoris." *Scribner's Magazine*, XCVII, No. 4 (April 1935).

679 "Smoke." *Harper's Magazine*, CLXIV (April 1932).

OTHER PRINTINGS

680 "Smoke." *The Best Short Stories of 1932 and The Yearbook of the American Short Story*, ed. Edward J. O'Brien. New York: Dodd, Mead, 1932.

DRAMATIC ADAPTATIONS

"Smoke." See 533 Gore Vidal, *Visit to a Small Planet and Other Television Plays*, 1957.

TRANSLATIONS—MISCELLANEOUS

681 "Dim." *Iz savremene americhke proze*. Belgrade: Novo Pokolene, 1954. Vol. II. Trans. into Serbian; translator not given.

682 "Spotted Horses." *Scribner's Magazine*, LXXXIX, No. 6 (June 1931).

OTHER PRINTINGS

683 "Spotted Horses." *Editor's Choice*, ed. Alfred Dashiell. New York: Putnam's, 1934.

684 ——. *The House of Fiction*, ed. Caroline Gordon and Allen Tate. New York: Scribner's, 1954. *The Hamlet* version.

685 ——. *Folklore in American Literature*, ed. John T. Flanagan and Arthur Palmer Hudson. Evanston, Ill.: Row, Peterson, 1958. *The Hamlet* version.

TRANSLATIONS

686 *Scheckige Mustangs*. Wiesbaden: Insel, 1956. Trans. Kurt Alboldt. Two copies. *The Hamlet* version.

687 "The Tall Men." *Saturday Evening Post*, CCXIII, No. 48 (May 31, 1941).

688 "That Evening Sun Go Down." *American Mercury*, XXII, No. 87 (March 1931). Two copies.

OTHER PRINTINGS

689 "That Evening Sun Go Down." *The Best Short Stories of 1931 and The Year Book of the American Short Story*, ed. Edward J. O'Brien. New York: Dodd, Mead, 1931.

690 "That Evening Sun." *Modern American Prose*, ed. Carl Van Doren. New York: Harcourt, Brace, 1934.

691 "That Evening Sun Go Down." *The Short Story Case Book*, ed. by Edward J. O'Brien. New York: Farrar and Rinehart, 1935. With commentary.

692 ——. *America's 93 Greatest Living Authors Present 'This Is My Best,'* ed. Whit Burnett. New York: Dial Press, 1942. Reprints a letter from Faulkner.

693 ——. *The American Mercury Reader*, ed. Lawrence E. Spivak and Charles Angoff. Philadelphia: Blakiston Co., 1944.

694 "That Evening Sun." *Modern Short Stories*, ed. Robert B. Heilman. New York: Harcourt, Brace, 1950.

695 ——. *50 Great Short Stories*, ed. Milton Crane. New York: Bantam, 1952.

696 ——. *Great Stories by Nobel Prize Winners*, ed. Leo Hamalian and Edmond L. Volpe. New York: Noonday, 1959.

697 ——. *Two and Twenty*, ed. Ralph H. Singleton. New York: St. Martin's, 1962.

698 "That Evening Sun Go Down." *Four American Writers of the Twentieth Century*, selected by Hans R. Faerber. Bern: A. Francke AG, 1962. From Collection of English Texts, LXXXII.

TRANSLATIONS

German

699 "Heute Nacht." *Neue Rundschau*, XLIV (May 1933). Trans. Käthe Rosenberg.

700 "Abendsonne." *Perspektiven*, VII (Summer 1954). Trans. Hermann Stresau.

Miscellaneous

701 "Akşam güneşi, batarken." *Beş (5) amerikan hikâyesi*. Istanbul: Varlik Yayinevi, 1952. Trans. Orhan Azizoğlu.

702 "Naar solen gaar ned." *Moderne amerikanske noveller*, ed. Ole Storm. Copenhagen: Thaning & Appels, 1954. Trans. Møller Kristensen.

703 ["That Evening Sun."] *18 wspolczesnych Opowiadan amerykanskich*. Warsaw: Iskry, 1957. Trans. Jan Zakrzewski.

704 "Solnedgång." *24 Nobelpristagare*. Stockholm: Folket i Bilds, 1960. Mårten Edlund.

RECORDINGS

"That Evening Sun." See 1018 tape recording for Recording for the Blind, Inc.

705 "That Will Be Fine." *American Mercury*, XXXV, No. 139 (July 1935).

OTHER PRINTINGS

706 "That Will Be Fine." *The Best Short Stories 1936 and The Yearbook of the American Short Story*, ed. Edward J. O'Brien. Boston–New York: Houghton Mifflin, 1936.

TRANSLATIONS

French

707 "C'est ça qui serait chic!" *Saint détective magazine*, No. 37 (March 1958). Trans. by Jeanne Fournier-Pargoire.

German

708 "Morgen, Kinder, wird's was geben." *Neu Amerika*, ed. Kurt Ullrich. Berlin: Fischer, 1937. Trans. Hermann Stresau.

709 [There Was a Queen.] Holograph manuscript, 5 pp. Incomplete. See Plate IV.

710 "There Was a Queen." *Scribner's Magazine*, XCIII, No. 1 (January 1933).

IV. First page of an incomplete five-page holograph manuscript entitled "There Was a Queen"

TRANSLATIONS—GERMAN

711 "Eine Königin." *Neue Rundschau*, XLIV, No. 10 (October 1933). Trans. Vivian Rodewald-Grebin. Xerox print.

712 "Thrift." *Saturday Evening Post*, CCIII, No. 10 (September 6, 1930).

OTHER PRINTINGS

713 "Thrift." *O. Henry Memorial Award Prize Stories of 1931*, ed. Blanche Colton Williams. Garden City: Doubleday, Doran, 1931.

714 "Tomorrow." *Saturday Evening Post*, CCXIII, No. 21 (November 23, 1940).

DRAMATIC ADAPTATIONS

715 *Tomorrow.* New York: Dramatists Play Service, 1963. Adapted by Horton Foote.

716 "Turn About." *Saturday Evening Post*, CCIV, No. 36 (March 5, 1932).

OTHER PRINTINGS

717 "Turn About." *O. Henry Memorial Award Prize Stories of 1932*, ed. Blanche Colton Williams. Garden City: Doubleday, Doran, 1932.

718 ——. *Great Modern Short Stories*, ed. with notes by Bennett A. Cerf. New York: Random House, n.d.

719 ——. *Men at War*, ed. with an introduction by Ernest Hemingway. New York: Crown Publishers, [1942].

720 "Two Soldiers." *Saturday Evening Post*, CCXIV, No. 39 (March 28, 1942).

OTHER PRINTINGS

721 "Two Soldiers." *O. Henry Memorial Award Prize Stories of 1942*, ed. Herschel Brickell. Garden City: Doubleday, Doran, 1942.

722 ——. *The Pocket Book of America*, ed. Philip Van Doren Stern. New York: Pocket Books, 1942.

723 ——. *Time to Be Young*, ed. Whit Burnett. Philadelphia–New York: Lippincott, 1945. Two copies.

724 ——. *The Best Short Stories of World War II*, ed. Charles A. Fenton. New York: Viking, 1957.

TRANSLATIONS

French

725 "Deux soldats." *Écrit aux U.S.A.: Anthologie des prosateurs américains du XX* siècle*, ed. Albert-J. Guérard. Paris: Laffont, 1947. Trans. R.-N. Raimbault.

Miscellaneous

726 "Två soldater." *Det bästas bokval.* Stockholm: Reader's Digest Aktiebolag, 1957.

727 "Dū sipahī." *Pap ki nagri*, comp. and trans. by Seyaida Nasīm Hamdani. Lahore, 1958.

728 "Uncle Willy." *American Mercury*, XXXVI, No. 124 (October 1935).

TRANSLATIONS—FRENCH

729 "Oncle Willy." *Revue de Paris*, LXIX, No. 1 (January 1962). Trans. R.-N. Raimbault. Xerox print.

730 "The Unvanquished." *Saturday Evening Post*, CCIX, No. 20 (November 14, 1936).

731 "Vendée." *Saturday Evening Post*, CCIX, No. 33 (December 5, 1936).

732 "Was." *Reading Fiction*, ed. with study material by Fred B. Millett. New York: Harper, 1950.

Illustrations of MSS, Typescripts, Etc.

Reproduction of typescript p. 1. See 2768 and 2766 Meriwether, "Career" and *Career*.

TRANSLATIONS—GERMAN

733 *Jagdglück*. Zurich: Arche, 1956. Trans. Elisabeth Schnack.

734 "Wash." *Harper's Magazine*, No. 1005 (February 1934).

OTHER PRINTINGS

735 "Wash." *O. Henry Memorial Award Prize Stories of 1934*, ed. Harry Hansen. Garden City: Doubleday, Doran, 1934.

736 ——. *Modern American Literature*, ed. Bernard J. Duffey. New York: Rinehart, 1951.

737 ——. *Great American Short Stories*, ed. Wallace and Mary Stegner. New York: Dell, 1957.

ITEMS in this section are listed chronologically by date of publication whether they are single poems or entire volumes of poems. Later printings, British editions, and translations, when there are any, follow the entry for first publication included here. Listed also are collections consisting of poems and early prose pieces and two dated typescripts of unpublished poems (in one case an unpublished version of a published poem).

738 "L'Après-Midi d'un Faune." *New Republic*, XX, No. 248 (August 6, 1919).

OTHER PRINTINGS

"L'Après-Midi d'un Faune." See 753 *Salmagundi*, 1932, and 770 *William Faulkner: Early Prose and Poetry*, ed. Carvel Collins, 1962.

739 "To a Co-ed." *Ole Miss*, Vol. XXIV, 1920.

OTHER PRINTINGS

"To a Co-ed." See 768 *Faulkner's University Pieces*, ed. Carvel Collins, 1962, and 770 *William Faulkner: Early Prose and Poetry*, ed. Carvel Collins, 1962.

740 "Portrait." *Double Dealer*, III, No. 18 (June 1922).

OTHER PRINTINGS

"Portrait." See 753 *Salmagundi*, 1932, and 770 *William Faulkner: Early Prose and Poetry*, ed. Carvel Collins, 1962.

741 "Mississippi Hills: My Epitaph." Typescript of an early version, four stanzas, typed signature, "William Faulkner, Oxford, Mississippi, October 17, 1924."

Unpublished. First line: "Far blue hills, where I pleasured me," See Plate V.

742 Typescript of an unpublished poem, no title, four stanzas, with typed signature, "William Faulkner, Oxford, Mississippi, October 18, 1924." First line: "Shall I recall this tree, when I am old," See Plate VI.

743 *The Marble Faun*
Boston: The Four Seas Company, [1924].
[1–3⁸ 4²], 26 ll.
pp. [1–6] 7–51 [52]. 19 cm.
Preface by Phil Stone.
Mottled green boards with printed labels on front and spine.
Copy 1: Printed dust jacket. Inscribed on free front endpaper, "To Miss Sally McGuire from W Faulkner"; signed on title page, "William Faulkner Oxford, Miss 24 December 1924"; also inscribed by Phil Stone, "Autographed for Mr. Raymond Green Oxford, Mississippi, April 15, 1932 Phil Stone." Copy 2: Inscribed on half title, "For Marion O'Donnell from William Faulkner"; signed on title page, "William Faulkner 31 October 1930"; also signed by Marion O'Donnell.
Only separate edition and printing.

OTHER PRINTINGS

744 The Marble Faun *and* A Green Bough. New York: Random House, [1965]. Reprint, "reproduced photographically from copies of the original editions." Two copies.

Illustrations of MSS, Typescripts, Etc.

Reproduction of carbon typescript of an unnumbered page. See 2766 Meriwether, *Career*.

745 "Dying Gladiator." *Double Dealer*, VII, No. 41–42 (January–February 1925). Contains also the essay "On Criticism."

MISSISSIPPI HILLS: MY EPITAPH.

Far blue hills, where I pleasured me,

Where on silver feet in dogwood cover

Spring follows, singing close the bluebird's"Lover!"

When to the road I trod an end I see;

Let this soft mouth, shaped to the rain,

Be but golden grief for grieving's sake,

And these green woods be dreaming here to wake

Within my heart when I return again.

Return I will! Where is there the death

While in these blue hills slumbrous overhead

I'm rooted like a tree? Though I be dead

This soil that holds me fast will find me breath.

The stricken tree has no young green to weep

The golden years we spend to buy regret.

So let this be my doom, if I forget

That there's still Spring to shake and break my sleep.

Oxford, Mississippi   William Faulkner
October 17, 1924.

V. Typescript of an early version of "Mississippi Hills: My Epitaph"

Shall I recall this tree, when I am old,

This hill, or how this valley filled with sun

And green afternoon was bought for morning's gold

And sold again for sleep when day is done?

As well to ask the wine to say what grapes

Distilled to purple suns when full and hot,

Or me what body hands' remembering shapes

To trouble heart when mind has long forgot.

The hushed wings of wind are feathered high

And shape the tree tops, vaguely fugitive,

To shake my heart with hill and vale for aye

When vale and hill itself no longer live.

But let me take this silver-minted moon

And bridle me the wind-centaurs that whirled

Out of Hellas, grained with beauty's noon,

And ride the cold old sorrow of the world.

Oxford, Mississippi,   William Faulkner.
October 18, 1924.

VI. Typescript of an unpublished poem dated October 18, 1924

THE
MARBLE FAUN

BY
WILLIAM FAULKNER

*William Faulkner
Oxford, Miss
24 Novs 1524*

BOSTON
THE FOUR SEAS COMPANY
PUBLISHERS

Title page of No. 743

OTHER PRINTINGS

"Dying Gladiator." See 753 *Salmagundi*, 1932, and 770 *William Faulkner: Early Prose and Poetry*, ed. Carvel Collins, 1962.

746   "The Faun." *Double Dealer*, VII, No. 43 (April 1925). Contains also the essay "Verse Old and Nascent: A Pilgrimage."

OTHER PRINTINGS

"The Faun." See 753 *Salmagundi*, 1932, and 770 *William Faulkner: Early Prose and Poetry*, ed. Carvel Collins, 1962.

747   "The Lilacs." *Double Dealer*, VII, No. 44 (June 1925).

OTHER PRINTINGS

748   "The Lilacs." *Anthology of Magazine Verse for 1925, and Yearbook of American Poetry*, ed. William Stanley Braithwaite. Boston: B. J. Brimmer, 1925.

——. See 753 *Salmagundi*, 1932.

"I." See 755 *The Green Bough*, 1933.

749   "The Lilacs." *Anthology of Magazine Verse for 1958* (ed. William Stanley Braithwaite) *and Anthology of Poems from the Seventeen Previously Published Braithwaite Anthologies* (ed. Margaret Haley Carpenter). New York: · Schulte, 1959. Copy signed by Braithwaite.

750   "I Will Not Weep for Youth"; "Twilight"; "Visions in Spring"; "April"; "To a Virgin"; "Winter Is Gone"; "My Epitaph"; "Knew I Love Once." *Contempo*, I, No. 17 (February 1, 1932). Two copies, one signed by Faulkner on the front page.

OTHER PRINTINGS

751   "I Will Not Weep for Youth"; "My Epitaph"; "To a Virgin"; "Winter Is Gone"; "Knew I Love Once"; "Twilight." *An Anthology of the Younger Poets*, ed. Oliver Wells. Philadelphia: Centaur Press, 1932.

752   "A Child Looks from His Window." *Contempo*, II, No. 2 (May 25, 1932).

753 *Salmagundi*

Under Faulkner's name appear two lines in italics: "and a Poem by Ernest M. Hemingway."

Milwaukee: The Casanova Press, 1932.

The following in red: "SALMAGUNDI," "Poem," "MCMXXXII"; the rest of the title page printed in black.

[1–3⁸ 4⁴], 28 ll.

pp. [1–6] 7–53 [54–56]. 23.7 cm.

Laid paper. Tan wrappers, printed in red and black. Boxed.

Certificate of limitation: ". . . strictly limited to 525 numbered copies, all to be sold . . . save 25 copies [260]," p. [54].

Note: In copies 1–26 the endpapers are flush with the top edge of the wrappers (see 2777 *First Editions of Twentieth Century Authors*, 1932).

Contains the following: *Poems*—"New Orleans," "The Faun," "Dying Gladiator," "Portrait," "The Lilacs," and "L'Après-Midi d'un Faune." *Criticism*—"On Criticism" and "Verse Old and Nascent: A Pilgrimage."

Only edition, only printing.

754 *This Earth*

New York: Equinox, 1932.

[1⁴], 4 ll., French fold.

pp. [1–8]. 20.4 cm.

Tan wrappers, printed in brown.

Revised version of "My Epitaph."

With drawings by Albert Heckman.

Copy 1: Beneath a signature of his name on the title page Faulkner has written, "This is a forgery signature. William Faulkner Keswick Va 6 March 1954"; and on p. [5], "ditto WF. William Faulkner." Copy 2: With an unprinted white envelope in which the pamphlet was issued. Copy 3.

Only edition, only printing.

755 *A Green Bough*

New York: Harrison Smith and Robert Haas, 1933.

[1–4⁸ 5⁴], 36 ll, 1 insert.

pp. [1–6] 7–67 [68–72]. 21.8 cm.

Laid paper, watermarked "Linweave Milano." Tan V-cloth, black-stamped on front and spine; two labels on front.

SALMAGUNDI

By

WILLIAM FAULKNER

and a Poem by

ERNEST M. HEMINGWAY

MILWAUKEE:

The CASANOVA PRESS

MCMXXXII

Title page of No. 753

Certificate of limitation: ". . . 360 copies, of which 350 are for sale . . . Number [183 William Faulkner]," p. [69].

Illustration pasted on inserted leaf facing title page, p. [3].

Forty-four numbered poems, fourteen of which had previous publication.

The limited and trade copies may be separate printings, but no priority has been established.

First edition, possibly first printing.

THIS EARTH

A POEM BY
WILLIAM FAULKNER

WITH DRAWINGS BY
ALBERT HECKMAN
EQUINOX, NEW YORK
I 9 3 2

Title page of No. 754

A GREEN BOUGH

BY WILLIAM FAULKNER

NEW YORK · NINETEEN THIRTY-THREE
HARRISON SMITH AND ROBERT HAAS

Title page of No. 755

756 ——

New York: Harrison Smith and Robert Haas, 1933. The illustration on the title page is blue-green.
[1–4⁸ 5⁴], 36 ll.
pp. [1–6] 7–67 [68–72]. 21.7 cm.
Laid paper, watermarked "Milton Laid." Green V-cloth, front blind-stamped and spine gold-stamped.
Trade edition.
Copy 1: Printed dust jacket; inscribed on free front endpaper, "To Byron Sage. William Faulkner," and signed on the title page, "William Faulkner Fox–20th Century Studio. California. 6 Jan. 1935." Copy 2: Printed dust jacket. Copy 3.
First edition, possibly second printing.

757 ——. New York: Smith & Haas, 1933. First edition, "Second printing, April 1933," possibly third printing.

OTHER PRINTINGS

See **744** The Marble Faun *and* A Green Bough, 1965.

Illustrations of MSS, Typescripts, Etc.

Reproduction of a galley. See 2790 Texas, *William Faulkner: An Exhibition of Manuscripts*, 1959.

American Excerpts

758 "Four Poems by William Faulkner." *New Republic*, LXXIV, No. 958 (April 12, 1933). Contains "Night Piece" ("VII" in *A Green Bough*); "Over the World's Rim" ("XXVIII"); "Gray the Day" ("XXX"); and "The Race's Splendor" ("XXXVII").

759 "The Ship of Night" ("XXXIV" in *A Green Bough*). *New Republic*, LXXIV, No. 959 (April 19, 1933).

760 "Man Comes, Man Goes" ("VI" in *A Green Bough*). *New Republic*, No. 961 (May 3, 1933).

761 "William Faulkner." *Mississippi Verse*, ed. Alice James. Chapel Hill: University of North Carolina Press, 1934. Contains "Mirror of Youth" ("XVI" in *A Green Bough*); "Boy and Eagle" ("XVII"); "Green Is the Water" ("XIX"); "Here He Stands" ("XX"); "Mother and Child" ("XXXIV"); "The Courtesan Is Dead" ("XXXV"); and "If There Be Grief" ("XLIV").

762 "Man Comes, Man Goes" ("VI" in *A Green Bough*). *New Republic Anthology: 1915-1935*, ed. Groff Conklin. New York: Dodge, 1936.

763 "The Race's Splendor" ("XXXVII" in *A Green Bough*). *40th Anniversary Issue New Republic 1914-1954*, CXXXI, No. 21 (November 22, 1954).

TRANSLATIONS

French

764 *Le rameau vert.* Paris: Gallimard, 1955. Trans. R.-N. Raimbault. English and French texts on facing pages. Copy 1: Copy E of 6 "hors commerce." Copy

2: Number 19 of 86. Copy 3: Number 165 of 500 "sur vélin Labeur."

Excerpts

765 "Poèmes." *Table ronde*, No. 37 (January 1951). Trans. R.-N. Raimbault. Poems V and XVIII.

German

766 *Ein grüner Zweig.* Stuttgart: Goverts, 1957. Trans. with afterword by Hans Hennecke. English and

Faulkner's
University Pieces

Compilation and Introduction
by
CARVEL COLLINS

Tokyo
Kenkyusha Limited

Title page of No. 768

German texts on facing pages. Includes twenty-five poems only.

767 ——. Zurich: Fretz & Wasmuth, 1957. Same as the Stuttgart edition.

768 *Faulkner's University Pieces*
Compilation and introduction by Carvel Collins.
Tokyo: Kenkyusha Limited, [1962].
[1–8⁸], 64 ll., 1 insert.
pp. [i–vi] vii–xii 1–114. 18.3 cm.
Dark blue cloth, spine gold-stamped. Printed dust jacket.
Photograph inserted facing title page, p. [iii]. Contains the following: *Poems*—"Cathay," "Sapphics," "After Fifty Years," "Une Ballade des Femmes Perdues," "Naiad's Song," "Fantouches," "Clair de Lune," "Streets," "A Poplar," "À Clymène," "Study," "Alma Mater," "To a Co-ed," "Co-education at Ole Miss," and "Nocturne." *Criticism*—Six reviews or essays under the title, "Books and Things," and with the subtitles, " 'In April Once' by W. A. Percy"; " 'Turns and Movies' by Conrad Aiken"; " 'Aria da Capo' by Edna St. Vincent Millay"; "American Drama: Eugene O'Neill"; "American Drama: Inhibitions"; and "Joseph Hergesheimer." *Short Stories*—"The Hill" and "Landing in Luck."
First edition, first printing?

769 *William Faulkner: Early Prose and Poetry*. Ed. Carvel Collins. Set of "unrevised, uncorrected galley proofs."

770 *William Faulkner: Early Prose and Poetry*
Compilation and introduction by Carvel Collins.
Boston: Little, Brown, [1962].
[1–8⁸ 9⁴ 10⁸], 30 ll.
pp. [i–viii] ix–xvi [1–2] 3–134 [135–136].
Light gray BF-cloth, spine maroon-stamped. Printed dust jacket. Copy 1 and copy 2.
Includes everything in *Faulkner's University Pieces* plus the following: *Poems*—"L'Après-Midi d'un Faune," "Portrait," "Dying Gladiator," and "The

Faun." *Criticism*—"On Criticism" and "Verse Old and Nascent: A Pilgrimage."
First edition, first printing.

BRITISH EDITIONS

771 *William Faulkner: Early Prose and Poetry*. Ed. Carvel Collins. London: Jonathan Cape, [1963]. Two copies.

ITEMS in this section are arranged chronologically by date of first publication, with later printings and excerpts following the individual articles.

772 "Ivory Tower." *The Mississippian* (The University of Mississippi), March 17, 1920.

773 *Sherwood Anderson & Other Famous Creoles: A Gallery of Contemporary New Orleans*
"Drawn by Wm. Spratling & arranged by Wm. Faulkner."
New Orleans: The Pelican Bookshop Press, 1926.
[1–3⁸ 4²], 26 ll.
pp. [1–52]. 21.1 cm.
Green boards with printed green label on front.
Certificate of limitation: "The first edition limited to 250 numbered copies . . ."
Copy 1: Number 14, one of the copies specially bound and tinted by Spratling. The boards have a design in orange, green, and white, with an all-over silver luster. Signed by Spratling on p. [1]. Copy 2: The certificate of limitation is covered with a printed label, "second issue 150 copies January 1927"; glassine dust jacket. Copy 3: Same as copy 2, signed "Faulkner" on the title page and inscribed "Fuck you, Jack" on p. [1]. Copy 4: Number 22, but the second-issue label has been removed, hence a sophisticated copy. Note that according to Daniel all 400 copies were printed on the same press run.
Foreward by Faulkner on pp. [7–8]. Sketch of Faulkner and Spratling, p. [49].

774 "His Name Was Pete." Oxford (Miss.) *Eagle*, August 15, 1946. Photostatic copy.

OTHER PRINTINGS

775 "His Name Was Pete." *Magazine Digest*, XXVI, No. 1 (January 1953).

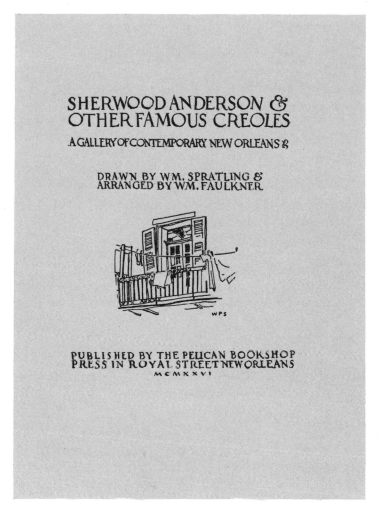

SHERWOOD ANDERSON &
OTHER FAMOUS CREOLES
A GALLERY OF CONTEMPORARY NEW ORLEANS &

DRAWN BY WM. SPRATLING &
ARRANGED BY WM. FAULKNER

PUBLISHED BY THE PELICAN BOOKSHOP
PRESS IN ROYAL STREET NEW ORLEANS
MCMXXVI

Title page of No. 773

776 "Mississippi." *Holiday*, XV, No. 4 (April 1954). Two copies.

OTHER PRINTINGS

777 "Mississippi." *Ten Years of Holiday*. New York: Simon & Schuster, 1956. Also uncorrected galley proof.

778 ——. *American Panorama East of the Mississippi.* Garden City: Doubleday, 1961.

779 ——. *Country Beautiful,* II, No. 2 (October 1962).

TRANSLATION

See 1012 *Shino tokoni yo kotawannte,* Vol. LXI, 1959. Trans. Masami Nishikawa.

780 "A Guest's Impression of New England." *New England Journeys Number 2,* Ford Times Special Edition, 1954. Two copies.

OTHER PRINTINGS

781 "A Guest's Impressions of New England." *The Ford Times Guide to Travel in U. S. A.,* ed. C. H. Dykeman. New York: Golden Press, 1962. Two copies.

782 "Sepulture South: Gaslight." *Harper's Bazaar,* LXXXI, No. 2917 (December 1954).

783 "An Innocent at Rinkside." *Sports Illustrated,* II, No. 4 (January 24, 1955). Three copies.

784 "Kentucky: May: Saturday." *Sports Illustrated,* II, No. 20 (May 16, 1955).

OTHER PRINTINGS

785 "Kentucky: May: Saturday." *Essays Today 2,* ed. Richard M. Ludwig. New York: Harcourt, Brace, 1956.

786 ——. *The Spectacle of Sport,* ed. Norton Wood. Englewood Cliffs, N.J.: Prentice-Hall, 1957.

787 "On Privacy: The American Dream: What Happened to It." *Harper's Magazine,* CCXI, No. 1262 (July 1955). American and also British issue.

788 *Impressions of Japan.* Tokyo: United States Information Service, [1955]. Mimeographed press release of six sheets; text on recto only. See Plate VII.

OTHER PRINTINGS

789 "Impressions of Japan." *Nippon Times,* August 22, 1955. Thermofax copy. In English.

——. See 1014 *Impressions of Japan,* 1955, and 885 *Faulkner at Nagano,* ed. Robert A. Jelliffe, 1956, and related entry.

Excerpts

790 "Japan Nothing Like West Faulkner Finds and Reports." Memphis *Commercial Appeal,* September 25, 1955. Part 1 of prose article. Positive and negative photostatic copies.

791 "Japanese Women Win High Praise from Faulkner for Fidelity, Industry." Memphis *Commercial Appeal,* October 2, 1955. Part 2 of prose article. Positive and negative photostatic copies; also Xerox copies.

792 *Nihon no seinen e* [To the Youth of Japan]
   Tokyo: United States Information Service, 1955. 20.8 cm.
   Cover title.
   [1⁶], 6 ll.
   pp. [i–ii] 1–8 [9–10].
   White wrappers, printed in tan and black.
   Text in Japanese and English.
   First edition, presumably first printing.

OTHER PRINTINGS

793 ["To the Youth of Japan."] *A Monthly Review of American Books. Bei kakidayori.* Tokyo: Cultural Office of the American Embassy, No. 30 (September 1955). Text in Japanese and English.

IMPRESSIONS OF JAPAN

By William Faulkner

(Prepared at Third Annual Summer Seminar in American Literature)

NAGANO CITY, August 1-21 -- The engines are long since throttled back;
the overcast sinks slowly upward with no semblance whatever of speed until
suddenly you see the aircraft's shadow scudding the cottony hillocks; and
now speed has returned again, aircraft and shadow now rushing toward one
another as toward one mutual headlong destruction.

To break through the overcast and fling that shadow once more down,
upon an island. It looks like land, like any other air found landfall, yet
you know it is an island, almost as if you saw both sea-bound flanks of it
at the same instant, like a transparent slide; an island more miraculously
found in the waste of water than Wake or Guam even, since here is a civili-
zation, an ordered and ancient homogeny of the human race.

It is visible and audible, spoken and written too: a communication
between man and man because humans speak it; you hear and see them. But
to this one Western ear and eye it means nothing because it resembles
nothing which that Western eye remembers; there is nothing to measure it
against, nothing for memory and habit to say, 'Say, this looks like the
word for house or home or happiness;' not even just cryptic but acrostic,

VII. First page of the press release of *Impressions of Japan*

797   "If I Were a Negro."   *White on Black*, ed. Era Bell Thomson and Herbert Nipson.   Chicago: Johnson Publishing Co., 1963.

日本の青年へ

ウィリアム・フォークナー

いまから百年前、私の国合衆国は経済的にも文化的にも一つの国ではなく、いずれが相手を支配するかを賭した戦いを九十五年前に交えたほど相反目する二つの部分にわかれていた。私の側であつた南部は、沖縄やガダルカナルが海をはるか隔てた島ではなくて本州か北海道の一部であつた場合のように、広漠とした大洋のなかの中立地帯ではなく、私たちの家、庭、畑のなかで戦われた幾多の戦闘のあつた戦争に敗れたのである。私たちの土地や家庭を荒した征服者は、私たちが敗北したのちまでも居止まつた。私たちは単に戦争に敗れただけではすまなかつた。敗北と降服につづく十年間に征服者は、戦後辛うじて私たちの手に残されたわずかなものまでも奪つてしまつた。この戦争の勝利者は私たちを人間社会、国家社会へ復帰させ、再興させる努力を全然しなかつた。

しかしいまでは、これらの事柄はいつさい過去のものとなつている。いまは私の国は一つである。むかし受けたこうした苦痛は、ただ一つになつたという以上に私の国を強固なものにしたと私は信じている。それはそのときの苦痛が私たちに、戦争

1

Cover title of No. 792

794   "On Fear: The South in Labor."   *Harper's Magazine*, CCXII, No. 1273 (June 1956).

795   "On Fear—The South in Labor."   *Gentlemen, Scholars and Scoundrels*, ed. Horace Knowles.   New York: Harper, 1959.

796   "If I Were a Negro."   *Ebony*, XI, No. 11 (September 1956).

ITEMS in this section are listed chronologically. For other critical articles see 768 and 770 *Faulkner's University Pieces*, 1962, and *William Faulkner: Early Prose and Poetry*, 1962, both edited by Carvel Collins.

798 "On Criticism." *Double Dealer*, VII, No. 41–42 (January–February, 1925). Contains also "Dying Gladiator".

OTHER PRINTINGS

"On Criticism." See 753 *Salmagundi*, 1932, and 770 *William Faulkner: Early Prose and Poetry*, ed. Carvel Collins, 1962.

799 "Verse Old and Nascent: A Pilgrimage." *Double Dealer*, VII, No. 43 (April 1925). Contains also "The Faun."

OTHER PRINTINGS

"Verse Old and Nascent: A Pilgrimage." See 753 *Salmagundi*, 1932, and 770 *William Faulkner: Early Prose and Poetry*, ed. Carvel Collins, 1962.

800 "Prophets of the New Age II— Sherwood Anderson." Dallas *Morning News*, April 26, 1925. Photostatic copy.

801 "Beyond the Talking." *New Republic*, LXVII, No. 859 (May 20, 1931). Review of Erich Maria Remarque's *The Road Back*.

802 "Folklore of the Air." *American Mercury*, XXXVI, No. 143 (November 1935). Review of Jimmy Collins' *Test Pilot*.

803 [Review of Ernest Hemingway's *The Old Man and the Sea*] *Shenandoah*, III, No. 3 (Autumn 1952).

804 "Sherwood Anderson. An Appreciation." *Atlantic Monthly*, CXCI, No. 6 (June 1953).

OTHER PRINTINGS

"Sherwood Anderson, An Appreciation." See 516 *Twelve American Writers*, ed. William M. Gibson and George Arms, 1962.

Brief Critical Comments

805 "Dark and Lonely," *Time*, XXXVII, No. 14 (April 7, 1941). On the burial of Sherwood Anderson, with a one-sentence tribute by Faulkner.

806 ["Yo escribo solamente . . ."] *Gaceta de literatura* (Mexico City), No. 9 (January–February 1952), p. 23. Contains the following quotation: "Yo escribo solamente cuando el espíritu me mueve; pero es que me mueve todos los días . . ."

807 "The Critic," *Newsweek*, XLIX, No. 21 (May 27, 1957). Faulkner is quoted on Hemingway.

ITEMS in this section are listed chronologically by date of delivery, with later printings following the first-publication entry. Included is the revised typescript of Faulkner's address to the Southern Historical Association at Memphis on November 10, 1955.

NOBEL PRIZE ADDRESS

808 *Les prix Nobel en 1950*
    Stockholm: Imprimerie Royale, P. A. Norstedt & Söner, 1951.
    [1⁸] 2–17⁸ 18¹⁰, 146 ll., 9 inserts.
    pp. [1–2] 3–281 [282], [1–2] 3–9 [10] (=292). 24 cm.
    Photographic leaves tipped in facing pp. 113, 116, 117, 119, 122, 124, 127, 128, 131.
    Copy 1: White wrappers printed in red on front and spine. Copy 2: Bound over wrappers. Blue S-cloth; gold-stamped on front and spine. All edges gold. In original glassine wrapper.
    The first official publication of the address, at pp. 71–72. The text here differs from the text of the *Herald Tribune* and Spiral Press publications.
    First edition, first printing.

809 " 'I Decline to Accept the End of Man.' " New York *Herald Tribune Book Review*, January 14, 1951.

810 "Nobel Prize Award Address." *Saturday Review*, XXXIV, No. 5 (February 3, 1951).

811 *William Faulkner's Speech of Acceptance upon the award of the Nobel Prize for Literature, delivered in Stockholm on the tenth of December, nineteen hundred fifty*
    New York: Spiral Press, 1951.
    Rule and initial "I" in red, the rest in black.
    [1⁶], 6 ll.
    pp. [1–12]. 24.6 cm.
    Beige wrappers, front printed in red and black.

LES PRIX NOBEL

EN 1950

AVEC UNE TABLE DES AUTEURS DES
ANNÉES 1901 à 1950.

STOCKHOLM
IMPRIMERIE ROYALE. P. A. NORSTEDT & SÖNER
1951

Title page of No. 808

Certificate of limitation: "Fifteen hundred copies of this Address were printed at The Spiral Press, New York in March 1951 for the friends of Random House and The Spiral Press."
    First separate edition, first printing.

OTHER PRINTINGS

812 *William Faulkner's Speech of Acceptance . . .* New York: Spiral Press, 1951. Certificate of limitation:

"Two thousand five hundred copies . . . March 1951
. . ."   First separate edition, second printing.

813 ——. Certificate of limitation: "Three thousand
five hundred copies . . . March 1951 . . ."   First separate edition, third printing.

814 "Nobel Prize Acceptance Address."   *Vogue*,
CXVII, No. 4 (March 1951).

William Faulkner's Speech of

Acceptance upon the award of the

Nobel Prize for Literature, deliv-

ered in Stockholm on the tenth of

December, nineteen hundred fifty.

I FEEL THAT THIS AWARD was not made
to me as a man, but to my work — a life's work in
the agony and sweat of the human spirit, not for
glory and least of all for profit, but to create out of
the materials of the human spirit something which did
not exist before. So this award is only mine in trust. It

First page of No. 811

---

815 McGrory, Mary.   "Reading and Writing."
Washington *Sunday Star*, April 29, 1951; clipping.
Contains a reprint of the Nobel Prize address.

816 *William Faulkner on Receiving the Nobel Prize.*
New York: Hunterdon Press, 1951.   Certificate of limi-
tation: "Two hundred copies . . . April, 1951 . . ."
Second separate edition, first printing.

817 "Faulkner's Credo."   *A.D.* (Flushing, N.Y.), II,
No. 1 (Spring 1951).

818 *I Decline to Accept the End of Man.*   Rochester:
Press of the Good Mountain, [1951].   Limited to 100
copies.

819 *William Faulkner's Speech of Acceptance upon
the award of the Nobel Prize for Literature, delivered in
Stockholm 10th December, 1950*
    London: Chatto & Windus.
    [1⁴], 28 ll.
    pp. [1–8].
    First British edition, first printing.

820 "Nobel Prize Acceptance Speech."   *Literary
Transition in the U.S.A.*   [New York?]: N.p., [1951?].

821 "William Faulkner's Speech of Acceptance . . ."
Gambit (Barbourville, Ky.), Spring 1952.   Two copies.

822 "On Accepting the Nobel Award."   *The Age of
Danger*, ed. Harold F. Harding.   New York: Random
House, [1952].

823 "Nobel Prize Acceptance Address."   *College
Reading*, ed. George Sanderlin.   Boston: Heath, 1953.

"Nobel Prize Address."   See 443 and 444 *The Faulkner
Reader*, 1954 and 1959.

824 "Nobel Prize Award Speech."   *A Southern
Reader*, ed. Willard Thorp.   New York: Knopf, 1955.

"Speech at Stockholm on the Occasion of His Receiving
the Nobel Prize."   See 885 *Faulkner at Nagano*, ed.
Robert A. Jelliffe, 1956.

VIII. Faulkner receiving the Nobel Prize for Literature from Gustaf VI Adolf in Stockholm, December 10, 1950

"William Faulkner's Speech of Acceptance . . ." See 308 *Soldiers' Pay*, 1959.

825 "Man Will Prevail." *Pulitzer Prize Reader*, ed. Leo Hamalian and Edmond L. Volpe. New York: Popular Library, 1961.

826 "Faulkner's Nobel Prize Speech." *Saturday Review*, XLV, No. 29 (July 28, 1962).

"Speech of Acceptance upon the Award of the Nobel Prize for Literature." See 516 *Twelve American Writers*, ed. William M. Gibson and George Arms, 1962, and 544 *Bear, Man and God*, ed. Francis Lee Utley *et al.*, 1964.

RECORDINGS

"The Nobel Prize Acceptance Speech." See 1013 *Faulkner Reads from His Works*, Caedmon TC 1035 (1954).

TRANSLATIONS

827 *William Faulkners Nobelpristale*. Copenhagen: Aschehoug, 1951. Trans. Kay Nielsen. 1300 copies printed. "Forfatteren William Faulkners tale holdt ved overrækkelsen af Nobel-prisen i litteratur i Stockholm, tiende december nitten hundrede og halvtreds."

828 "Je me refuse à admettre la fin de l'homme." *Profiles littérature, art, musique des États-Unis*, I, No. 1 (October 1952). Trans. L. Jacoël.

Excerpts

829 ". . . Der Junge Mensch, Der Heute Schreibt . . ." *Lyrik der Welt*, ed. Reinhard Jaspert. Berlin: Safari, 1953. Trans. Donata Helmrich-Hardt.

———

"Speech of Acceptance on Being Made an Officer of the Legion of Honor, October 26, 1951," reproduction of holograph MS. See 2769 Meriwether, "Check List."

830 "Never Be Afraid . . ." *Harvard Advocate*, CXXXV, No. 2 (November 1951). Commencement address, University High School, Oxford, Miss., on May 28, 1951. Four copies.

OTHER PRINTINGS

831 "Commencement Address." *Middle South News* (New Orleans), Summer 1962.

832 *An Address Delivered by William Faulkner*
Delta Council Annual Meeting, Delta State Teachers College Campus, Cleveland, Miss., 1952.
[1⁴], 4 ll.
pp. [1–8]. 21.7 cm.
Green wrappers, printed in black. Two copies.
First edition.

OTHER PRINTINGS

833 "The Rights of Man." *Delta Review*, II, No. 3 (1965).

834 *Commencement Address*. Pine Manor Junior College, Wellesley, Mass., June 8, 1953. Mimeographed press release. 11 sheets, text on recto only. First edition, first printing, of the full version.

835 ———. N.d. Mimeographed press release. 10 sheets, text on recto only. Second edition.

OTHER PRINTINGS

836 "Faith or Fear." *Atlantic Monthly*, CIXII, No. 2 (August 1953). Two copies.

Excerpts

837 "Final Fanfare for '53." *Life*, XXXIV, No. 25 (June 22, 1953).

838 *Address of William Faulkner*. New York, 1955. Mimeographed press release. Two sheets, text on recto only. National Book Award Acceptance Address. See Plate IX.

An
Address Delivered

By

William Faulkner

Oxford, Mississippi

At The

Seventeenth Annual Meeting

Of

DELTA COUNCIL

May 15, 1952

Delta State Teachers College Campus,
Cleveland, Mississippi

Title page of No. 832

OTHER PRINTINGS

839 "Treasure Chest." New York *Times Book Review*, February 6, 1955, pp. 2, 24.

840 "National Book Award Acceptance Address." *Saturday Review*, XLV, No. 29 (July 28, 1962).

TRANSLATIONS

841 "Konstnären och samhället." *All världens berättare*, XI, No. 4 (April 1955). Trans. Mårten Edlund.

842 "Remarks of William Faulkner at Meeting of Southern Historical Association, Memphis, Tennessee, November 19 [*sic*], 1955." Revised original typescript, 8 p. With accompanying letter by Dr. James W. Silver.

843 "American Segregation and the World Crisis." *The Segregation Decisions*
    Atlanta· Southern Regional Council, 1956.
    1^{16}, 16 ll.
    pp. [1–4] 5–7 [8] 9–29 [30–32].
    Pale gray wrappers, printed on front and back in green. This text adds three paragraphs to the speech as delivered. Two copies.
    First edition, first printing.
    Faulkner's address to the Southern Historical Association on November 10, 1955, in Memphis, with addresses by Benjamin E. Mays and Cecil Sims and a foreword by Bell I. Wiley.

844 ——. Atlanta: Southern Regional Council, 1956. Off-white wrappers, printed in green. First edition, "second printing."

845 "Equal Right to Opportunity Emphasized in Faulkner Text." Memphis *Commercial Appeal*, November 11, 1955. Address given at dinner session of the 21st annual meeting of the Southern Historical Association in Memphis.

Address of William Faulkner
National Book Award
New York City
January 25, 1955

HOLD FOR RELEASE
6 p.m. Tuesday, January 25, 1955

By artist I mean of course everyone who has tried to create something which was not here before him, with no other tools and material than the un-commerciable ones of the human spirit; who has tried to carve, no matter how crudely, on the wall of that final oblivion, in the tongue of the human spirit, 'Kilroy was here.'

That is primarily, and I think in its essence, all that we ever really tried to do. And I believe we will all agree that we failed. That what we made never quite matched and never will match the shape, the dream of perfection which we inherited and which drove us and will continue to drive us, even after each failure, until anguish frees us and the hand falls still at last.

Maybe it's just as well that we are doomed to fail, since, as long as we do fail and the hand continues to hold blood, we will try again; where, if we ever did attain the dream, match the shape, scale that ultimate peak of perfection, nothing would remain but to jump off the other side of it into suicide. Which would not only deprive us of our American right to existence, not only inalienable but harmless too, since by our standards, in our culture, the pursuit of art is a peaceful hobby like breeding Dalmatians, it would leave refuse in the form of, at best indigence and at worst downright crime resulting from unexhausted energy, to be scavenged and removed and disposed of. While this way, constantly and steadily occupied by, obsessed with, immersed in trying to do the impossible, faced always with the failure which we decline to recognize and accept, we stay out of trouble, keep out of the way of the practical and busy people who carry the burden of America.

IX. First page of the press release of Faulkner's National Book Award Acceptance Address

The Segregation Decisions

PAPERS READ AT A SESSION OF THE
TWENTY-FIRST ANNUAL MEETING OF THE
SOUTHERN HISTORICAL ASSOCIATION,
MEMPHIS, TENNESSEE, NOVEMBER 10, 1955

WILLIAM FAULKNER

BENJAMIN E. MAYS

CECIL SIMS

With a Foreword by
BELL I. WILEY

SOUTHERN REGIONAL COUNCIL, ATLANTA, GEORGIA, 1956

First page of No. 843

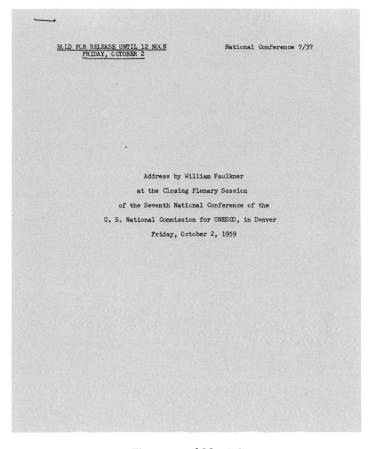

First page of No. 848

846 "A Word to Virginians." *University of Virginia Magazine*, II, No. 2 (Spring 1958). Two copies. An address before the Raven Society, OΔK, and the Jefferson Society of the University of Virginia on February 20, 1958. Also an announcement of the address.

847 "Presentation to John Dos Passos of the Gold Medal for Fiction." *Proceedings of the American* *Academy of Arts and Letters*, Second Series, No. 8. New York, 1958.

848 *Address by William Faulkner at the Closing Plenary Session of the Seventh National Conference of the U. S. National Commission for UNESCO.* Denver, October 2, 1959. Mimeographed press release. 3 sheets, text on recto only. First edition. Three copies.

OTHER PRINTINGS

849 "From Yoknapatawpha to UNESCO, the Dream." *Saturday Review*, XLII, No. 46 (November 14, 1959).

850   "Acceptance by William Faulkner of Gold Medal
Award, American Academy of Arts and Letters" (May
24, 1962).   *Proceedings of the American Academy of
Arts and Letters*, Second Series, No. 13.   New York,
1963.

851   "Faulkner: Thoughts   on   Life   and   Liberty."
New York *Times*, April 18, 1965, p. X21.   Excerpts
from Faulkner's novels and speeches as prepared for
"William Faulkner's Mississippi," a television broadcast
on WNEW, New York, Friday, April 23, 1965.   Also
an advertisement for this program from the New York
Herald Tribune, April 23, 1965.

THE first part of this section is arranged alphabetically by the name of the person interviewing Faulkner. When Faulkner is talking to large groups, the material is listed under the name of the editor. The second part, consisting of unsigned interviews, is arranged chronologically.

SIGNED INTERVIEWS AND EDITED BOOKS

852 Allen, R. M. "Notes on William Faulkner." Transcription of a classroom interview, University of Mississippi, Spring 1947. Photostat copy, with photostat copy of letter from Allen. Also, mimeographed copy of interview, with accompanying original letter from Allen laid in.

853 Arban, Dominique. "Je ne sais rien des gens réels . . ." *Figaro littéraire*, December 16, 1950.

854 Bouvard, Loïc. "Conversation with William Faulkner." *Modern Fiction Studies*, V, No. 4 (Winter 1959–1960). Trans. Henry Dan Piper.

855 Boyle, Hal. "Success comes too easy." Charlottesville (Va.) *Daily Progress*, May 12, 1955.

856 Breit, Harvey. "A Walk with Faulkner." New York *Times Book Review*, January 30, 1955.

OTHER PRINTINGS

857 "An Interview with Harvey Breit." *The Writer Observed*. Cleveland–New York: World, 1956.

858 Brierre, Annie. "Dernière rencontre avec Faulkner." *Nouvelle littéraire*, July 12, 1962.

859 ——. "Faulkner parle." *Nouvelles littéraires, artistiques et scientifiques*, No. 1466 (October 6, 1955).

860 Castiglione, Luigi. "Il suo pensiero sull'uomo e sull'arte:—Conversazione con Faulkner." *Fiera letteraria*, July 22, 1962.

861 Chapsal, Madeleine. "A Lion in the Garden." *The Reporter*, November 3, 1955. "Advance proof copy."

862 Chaze, Elliott. "Visit to a Two-fingered Typist." *Life*, LII, No. 2 (July 14, 1961). Various comments on "Visit to a Two-fingered Typist" appeared in "Letters to the editor," *Life*, LII, No. 5 (August 4, 1961).

863 Claxton, Simon. "William Faulkner: An Interview." *Cate Review*, June 1962.

864 Dahlgren, Nils. "Faulkner—la dernière interview." *L'express*, July 19, 1962.

OTHER PRINTINGS

865 "Interview." *Books and Bookmen*, September 1962.

866 Fant, Joseph L., and Ashley, Robert, eds. *Faulkner at West Point*. New York: Random House, [1964].

TRANSLATIONS

867 Fant, Joseph L., and Ashley, Robert, eds. *Faulkner op West Point:* Utrecht: A. W. Bruna & Zoon, n.d. Trans. O. Falk. Paperback.

X. Faulkner holding a news conference in Paris, September 19, 1955

868 Grenier, Cynthia. "An Interview with Cynthia Grenier." *Accent*, XVI (Summer 1956).

TRANSLATIONS

869 "Dialogue de William Faulkner avec Cynthia Grenier." *Table ronde*, No. 109 (January 1957).

870 Guth, Paul. "En remontant avec Faulkner les chemins de la vie et ceux de l'écriture." *Figaro littéraire*, October 8, 1955.

Gwynn, Frederick L., and Blotner, Joseph L., comps. See 1016 "Faulkner in the University," 1957-1958, and 1017 *Faulkner at Virginia*, 1960.

871 ——, eds. "Faulkner in the University, A Classroom Conference." *College English*, XIX, No. 1 (Winter 1957).

872 ——. *Faulkner in the University: Class Conferences at the University of Virginia 1957-1958*. Two sets of galley proof. Two sets of page proof. Signatures.

873 ——. Charlottesville, Va.: The University of Virginia Press, 1959. Advance copy.

874 ——. 1959. 23 cm. First edition, first printing. Two copies.

875 ——. New York: Vintage Books (Random House), [1965]. "First Vintage Edition February 1965."

TRANSLATIONS

French

876 Gwynn, Frederick L., and Blotner, Joseph L., eds. *Faulkner à l'Université*. Paris: Gallimard, [1964]. Trans. René Hilleret, with introduction by J. Gresset. Copy "sur vélin pur fil Lafuma-Navarre," No. 9. Trade edition; 2 copies.

Excerpts

877 "Le fin de William Faulkner." *Express LU*, March 5, 1964.

FAULKNER
in the University
Class Conferences at the University of Virginia 1957-1958

Edited by
FREDERICK L. GWYNN
and
JOSEPH L. BLOTNER

1959
Charlottesville, Virginia
THE UNIVERSITY OF VIRGINIA PRESS

Title page of No. 874

878 Hilleret, René. "Colloques en Virginie avec William Faulkner." *Revue de Paris*, No. 2 (February 1964). *164548*

German

879 Gwynn, Frederick L., and Blotner, Joseph L., eds. *Gespräche mit Faulkner*. Stuttgart: Goverts, 1961. Trans. Helmut Hilzheimer.

XI. Faulkner at a student conference at the University of Virginia, 1957–58

880 ——. Zurich: Fretz & Wasmuth, 1961. The Hilzheimer translation.

881 Gwynn, Frederick L., and Blotner, Joseph L. "William Faulkner on Dialect." *University of Virginia Magazine*, II, No. 1 (Winter 1958).

882 Howe, Russell Warren. "A Talk with William Faulkner." *The Reporter*, XIV, No. 6 (March 22, 1956).

Excerpts

883 "Faulkner: 'I'd Fight for Mississippi.'" *U.S. News & World Report*, LII (October 15, 1962).

884 Hutchens, John K. "On the Books." New York *Herald Tribune Book Review*, October 31, 1948.

885 Jelliffe, Robert A., ed. *Faulkner at Nagano*. Tokyo: Kenkyusha, [1956]. 18.3 cm. First edition, first printing? This includes 788 *Impressions of Japan*, 1955. Two copies.

Excerpts

886 "Faulkner in Japan." *Esquire*, L, No. 6 (December 1958). This includes 788 *Impressions of Japan*, 1955.

887 Marković, Vida. "Poslednji intervju velikog američkog pistsa: Susret sa Foknerom." Belgrade *Borba*, July 8, 1962; clipping. Typescript of a translation by Vida Janković attached.

TRANSLATIONS

888 "Interview with Faulkner." *Texas Studies in Literature and Language*, V, No. 4 (Winter 1964).

889 Nishikawa, Masami. "Plot Complications Result

FAULKNER AT NAGANO

Edited by

ROBERT A. JELLIFFE

FULBRIGHT LECTURER IN KOBE COLLEGE

TOKYO

KENKYUSHA LTD.

Title page of No. 885

of His ignorance . . ." Osaka (Japan) *Mainichi*, August 7, 1955.

OTHER PRINTINGS

See 885 *Faulkner at Nagano*, ed. Robert A. Jelliffe, 1956, and 2660 Leon Picon's scrapbook.

890 Nishikawa, Masami. "Man and His Problems— William Faulkner's Aims." Osaka (Japan) *Mainichi*, August 18, 1955.

OTHER PRINTINGS

See 885 *Faulkner at Nagano,* ed. Robert A. Jelliffe, 1956, and 2660 Leon Picon's scrapbook.

891   Philippine Writers Association. *faulkner on truth and freedom.* [Manila?: The Association, 1955?] 13 x 17.9 cm. Excerpts from tape recordings. First edition, first printing.

Title page of No. 891

892   Rascoe, Lavon. "An Interview with William Faulkner." *Western Review,* XV, No. 4 (Summer 1951).

893   Stein, Jean. "The Art of Fiction XII: William Faulkner." *Paris Review,* IV, No. 12 (Spring 1956).

UNSIGNED INTERVIEWS

901   "Slavery Better for the Negro, Says Faulkner." New York *Herald Tribune,* November 14, 1931.

902   "Doom." *New Yorker,* February 28, 1953.

903   "Faulkner Hits Killing of Negro, 14." New York

Contains also reproductions of the self-portrait by Faulkner and of the first MS page of *As I Lay Dying.* Leading article from *Times Literary Supplement* laid in. Also page proofs.

OTHER PRINTINGS

894   "Faulkner Interviewed." *Quest* (Bombay), II, No. 1 (August–September 1956). Slightly abridged.

895   "William Faulkner." *Writers at Work,* ed. Malcolm Cowley, New York: Viking Press, 1958.

896   ——. 1959. Paperback reprint.

Excerpts

897   "Talker." *Time,* LXVII, No. 22 (May 28, 1956). Contains also a footnote giving a later comment by Faulkner.

898   *Saturday Review,* XLV, No. 29 (July 28, 1962).

"Interview in New York in Early 1956." See 516 *Twelve American Writers,* ed. William M. Gibson and George Arms, 1962.

TRANSLATIONS—GERMAN—EXCERPTS

See 403 Wilde Palmen *und* Der Strom, 1957.

899   Trédant, Paul. "Faulkner à Paris." *Nouvelles littéraires,* December 14, 1950.

900   Wyllie, John Cook. "Prides and Prejudices: Conversations with William Faulkner." Richmond *News Leader,* January 31, 1955.

Herald Tribune, September 11, 1955. Photostatic copy.

904   "Visit with the Author." *Newsweek,* CIII, No. 58 (February 9, 1959). On the play *Requiem for a Nun.*

LETTERS are divided into two categories: those intended for publication and those not so intended. In each cate-gory they are arranged chronologically or, when un-dated, approximately so.

INTENDED FOR PUBLICATION

905 Letter to the Editor. *The Mississippian* (The University of Mississippi), April 7, 1920.

906 Letter to the Book Editor, Miss Fanny Butcher. Chicago *Tribune*, July 16, 1927.

OTHER PRINTINGS

907 [Letter to Miss Fanny Butcher.] *Studi americani*, IX (1964).

908 [Letters to Casanova Booksellers.] *First Editions of Twentieth Century Authors*. Milwaukee: Casanova Booksellers, 1932. Comment on himself (December 1931, p. 22) and on Hemingway's comment on him (n.d., also p. 22).

909 [Reply to a questionnaire from the League of American writers.] *Writers Take Sides*. New York: League of American Writers, 1938. Two copies. "Letters about the war in Spain from 418 American authors."

910 Letter to the Editor. Memphis *Commercial Appeal*, July 12, 1941.

911 ——. Oxford (Miss.) *Eagle*, March 13, 1947.

912 ——. Memphis *Commercial Appeal*, March 26, 1950.

913 ——. April 9, 1950.

914 ——. Oxford (Miss.) *Eagle*, September 14, 1950.

915 ——. *Time*, LVI, No. 20 (November 13, 1950).

916 "Letter of Acknowledgment from William Faulkner." *Proceedings of the American Academy of Arts and Letters*, Second Series, No. 1. New York, 1951. On the presentation of the Howells Medal to Faulkner.

917 Letter to the Editor. New York *Times*, December 26, 1954.

918 ——. Memphis *Commercial Appeal*, February 20, 1955. Reprinted in "In and Out of Books," New York *Times Book Review*, Section 7, March 13, 1955.

919 ——. March 20, 1955.

920 ——. New York *Times*, March 25, 1955.

921 ——. Memphis *Commercial Appeal*, April 3, 1955.

922 ——. April 10, 1955.

923 ——. April 17, 1955.

924 "A Letter to the North." *Life*, XL, No. 10 (March 5, 1956).

OTHER PRINTINGS

925 "A Letter to the North." *Reader's Digest*, No. 409 (May 1956). Condensed.

926 ——. *Virginia Spectator*, CXVIII (May 1957).

927 ——. *A Reading Approach to Writing*, ed. Martha Heasley Cox and Dorothy Norris Foote. San Francisco: Chandler, 1962. With *Aids for Teaching*.

928 "Integration Warning—Faulkner Asked for Slower Pace." Dallas *Morning News*, July 28, 1963.

Illustrations of MSS, Typescripts, Etc.

"Letter to a Northern Editor." Reproduction of typescript p. 1 with authorial revisions. See 2766 Meriwether, *Career*.

929 Letter to the Editor. *Life*, XL, No. 13 (March 26, 1956).

930 ——. *The Reporter*, XIV, No. 8 (April 19, 1956).

931 ——. *Time*, LXVII, No. 17 (April 23, 1956).

932 ——. *Time*, LXVIII, No. 24 (December 10, 1956).

933 ——. New York *Times*, December 16, 1956.

934 ——. *Time*, LXIX, No. 6 (February 11, 1957).

935 ——. Memphis *Commercial Appeal*, September 15, 1957. Two copies.

936 ——. New York *Times*, October 13, 1957.

NOT INTENDED FOR PUBLICATION

937 Typescript letter to the Four Seas Co., June 20, 1923. One page, signed "William Faulkner." On verso: "United States Post Office, University, Mississippi." Transmits MS entitled "Orpheus and Other Poems." Reply from publisher, June 26, 1923, laid in. Addressed to William Faulkner, University, Mississippi, suggesting that if he will pay the manufacturing costs Four Seas might be willing to undertake publication of the book.

938 Typescript letter to Four Seas Co. (November 1923). One page, signed "William Faulkner." Carbon copy of publisher's reply laid in. Inquiries about receipt of his MS "Orpheus."

939 Typescript letter to Four Seas Co., November 23, 1923. One page, signed "William Faulkner." Requests return of MS.

940 Typescript letter to Four Seas Co., July 19, 1924. One page, signed "William Faulkner." Offers to put up $400 against publication costs. Carbon copy of publisher's reply, which agrees to a November 1 publication date provided contract is signed within the next week or so.

941 Typed note, no salutation, no addressee (1924). One page, signed "W. Faulkner." Request insertion of a dedication, "To my mother" (in *The Marble Faun*).

942 Typescript letter to Four Seas Co., September 9, 1924, Oxford. One page, signed "William Faulkner." Encloses, as requested, two photographs and a one-page biographical sketch. The biographical sketch was unquestionably typed by Faulkner, who states therein that *The Marble Faun* was written in the spring of 1919.

Typescript letter to Sherwood Anderson (1926?). Three pages, with typed signature. Reproduced as illustrations. See 2766 Meriwether, *Career*.

943 Holograph letter to Ben (Wasson), n.d. Two pages. On the use of colored inks in *The Sound and the Fury*. See Plate XII.

944 Holograph letter, no salutation, n.d. One page, signed "Bill." List of seventeen prospective purchasers (of *The Sound and the Fury*).

945 Typescript letter to "The Editors" of the *Saturday Evening Post*, n.d. (postmarked November 9, 1930). One page, typed signature, with original envelope addressed in Faulkner's handwriting. After mailing the story, he says, he decided to make changes in the beginning of "Rose of Lebanon."

946 Typescript letter to "Mr. [Alfred] Dashiell," January 30, 1931, Oxford. One page, signed "William Faulkner." Says he is rewriting the "horse story" ("Spotted Horses") and regrets that Dashiell did not like the story about the "Jew wing-walker" ("Death Drag").

947 Typescript letter to James Southall Wilson, September 24, 1931. One page, signed "William Faulkner." Accepts invitation to Writers' Conference.

948 Holograph letter to James Southall Wilson; October 5, 1931, Oxford. One page, five lines, signed "William Faulkner." Discusses arrival in Charlottesville.

949 Xerox copy of holograph letter to Ben (Wasson, 1931, Oxford). One page, signed "Bill." Says he is having trouble writing Bennett's introduction. Original owned by H. Richard Archer.

950 Xerox copy of holograph letter to Ben (Wasson, 1931, Oxford). One page, signed "Bill." Says he has just sold two stories to the *Post* for $1,250; has bought the old Baily place; hopes to continue work on a novel; is considering appeal by "Hal" (Harrison Smith) to come to New York City. Original owned by H. Richard Archer.

951 Xerox copy of holograph letter to Ben (Wasson, 1931, Oxford). One page, signed "Bill." Faulkner asks Wasson to check with his publisher for a much delayed statement. Also xerox copy of envelope addressed in Faulkner's handwriting to "Mr. Ben Wasson" in New York City. Postal mark reads "Oxford Dec. 16" (1931). Originals owned by H. Richard Archer.

952 Xerox copy of holograph letter to Ben (Wasson, 1931, Oxford). One page, signed "Bill." Says another story is enclosed. Original owned by H. Richard Archer.

953 Xerox copy of holograph letter to Ben (Wasson, 1931, Oxford). One page, signed "Bill." Requests help in handling an unspecified business matter. Original owned by H. Richard Archer.

954 Holograph letter to Ben (Wasson), n.d. (but marked "received 1/26/32"). One page, nine lines, signed "Bill." Says *Light in August* is not yet typed.

Reproduction of a typescript letter to Maurice Coindreau, April 14, 1932, Oxford. One page, signed "William Faulkner." See 2769 Meriwether, "Check List." Concerns French translation of "Dry September."

Dear Ben —

Thank you for the letter.

I received the proof. It seemed pretty tough to me, so I corrected it as written, adding a few more italics where the original seemed obscure on second reading. Your reason for the change, i.e., that with italics only 2 different dates were indicated I do not think sound for 2 reasons. First, I do not see that the use of breaks clarifies it any more; Second, there are more than 4 dates involved. The ones I recall offhand / are: Damuddy dies. Benjy is 3. ② His name is changed. He is 5. ③ Caddy's wedding. He is 14. ④ He tries to rape a young girl and is castrated. 15. ⑤ Quentin's death. ⑥ The father's death. ⑦ A visit to the cemetery at 18. ⑦ The day of the anecdote, he is 33. These are just a few I recall, so your reason explodes itself.

But the main reason is, a break indicates an objective change in tempo, while the objective picture here should be a continuous whole, since the thought transference is subjective; i.e., in Ben's mind and not in the reader's eye. I think italics are necessary to establish for the reader Benjy's confusion; that unbroken-surfaced confusion of an idiot which is outwardly a dynamic and logical

XII. Two-page letter to Ben Wasson about *The Sound and the Fury*

coherence. To gain this, by using breaks it will be necessary to write an induction for each transference. I wish publishing was advanced enough to use colored ink for such, as I argued with you and that in the speak-easy that day. But the form in which you now have it is pretty tough. It presents a most dull and poorly articulated picture to my eye. If something must be done, it were better to re-write this whole section objectively, like the 415 section. I think it is rotten, as is. But if you want have it so, I'll just have to save the idea until publishing grows up to it. Anyway, change all the italics. You overlooked one of them. Also, the parts written in italics will all have to be punctuated again. You'd better see to that, since you're all for coherence. And don't make any more additions to the script, bud. I know you mean well, but so do I. I effaced the 2 or 3 you made.

We have a very pleasant place on the beach here. I swim and fish and row a little. Estelle sends love.

I hope you will think better of this. Your reason above disproves itself. I purposely used italics in both actual scenes and remembered scenes in the reason, not to indicate the different dates of happenings, but never to permit the reader to anticipate a transfel. Transference, without reference to both the recollection postulate its own date. Savvy you see this.

To F. H. Lewis,
Pascagoula, Miss

Bill

955 Holograph letter to Ben (Wasson, 1932). One page, signed "Bill." Is sending MS for October publication or later.

956 Holograph letter to Ben (Wasson), dated by a nonauthorial hand September 25, 1932. One page. About *Light in August*.

957 Holograph letter to Ben (Wasson), n.d. One page, five lines, signed "Bill." "Here is what I received re Cape & Smith."

958 Holograph letter, no salutation (to Ben Wasson), n.d. (marked in nonauthorial hand "June 27, 1933."). One page, signed "Bill." About birth of his daughter. Mentions the proposed colored-ink version of *The Sound and the Fury* and an introduction he is scheduled to write; he is presently at work on a novel.

959 Typescript letter to Ben (Wasson), n.d. One page, with six lines in ink added. About his work, growing baby, and more checks.

960 Typescript letter to Ben (Wasson), n.d. One page, with typed signature "Bill." Discusses revisions in proof of his short story ("Beyond").

961 Typescript letter to Ben (Wasson), n.d. One page, signed "Bill." Sending story to *Harper's*.

962 Typescript letter to Morty (Goldman), n.d. One page, signed "Faulkner." Encloses rewritten story, "Drusilla"; has mailed another book to Smith in MS, possibly *Pylon*.

963 Typescript letter, no salutation, July 29, Oxford. One page, signed in pencil "Faulkner." Has been in California working on a movie script.

964 Typescript letter to Morty (Goldman), February 18, 1935, Oxford. One page, signed in pencil "Faulkner." Says that his brother (John) is working on a story. Declines to undertake a book on the Mississippi River. Wants Goldman to prevent publication by the Centaur Press of "The Marionettes," of which he produced six copies by hand.

965 Typescript letter, no salutation, March 9, 1935. One page, with one holograph line in pencil; signed "Faulkner." Discusses contract arrangements.

966 Typescript note to Morty (Goldman), n.d. One page, pencil signature, "Faulkner." "Enclosed is another of the best short story in 1935."

967 Typescript letter to Morty (Goldman), September 4, 1936, on letterhead of Twentieth Century–Fox Film Corporation. One page, signed "Bill." Will try to sell book to the "pictures."

968 Holograph letter to Morty (Goldman), December 28, no year, on letterhead of Twentieth Century–Fox Film Corporation. One page, five lines. Nothing on hand to sell; will write more stories and a novel.

969 Holograph note to Morty (Goldman), n.d. One page, signed "F." About story sent to the *Post*.

970 Typescript letter to Morty (Goldman), n.d. One page, signed "Faulkner." On price for a series of stories for the *Post*.

971 Typescript letter to Morty (Goldman), n.d. One page, signed "Faulkner." Reports he is working on a story for the *Post*.

972 Typescript letter to Morty (Goldman), n.d. One page, signed "Faulkner." Approves $900 for *Post* story. Will write Smith about "Bear Hunt."

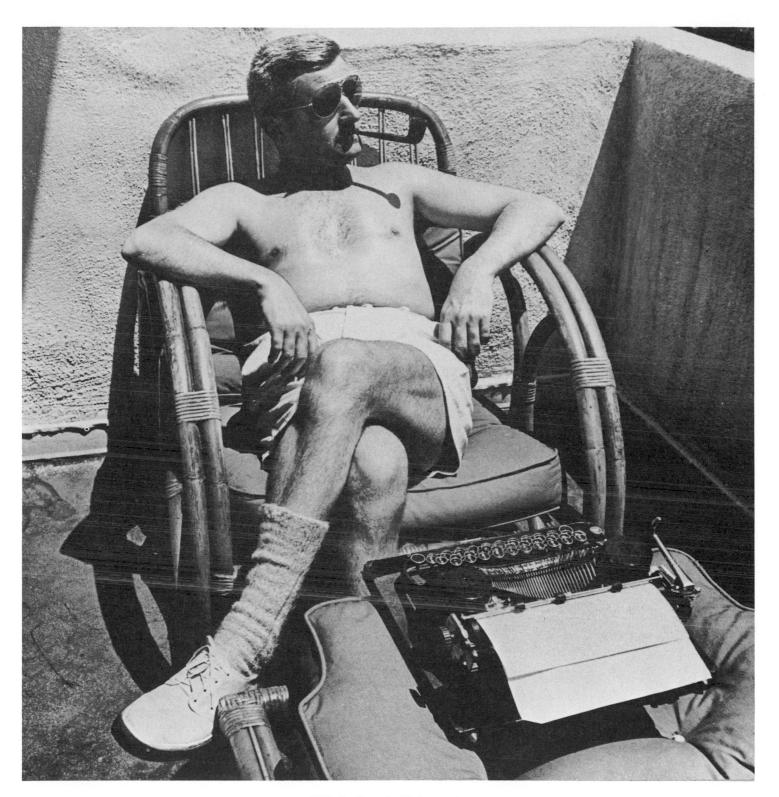

XIII. Faulkner in Hollywood

973   Typescript letter to Morty (Goldman), December 4, no year. One page, signed "Faulkner." Says novel almost completed; has contract with movies.

974   Typescript letter to Morty (Goldman), n.d. One page, signed "Faulkner," with four lines in ink added. Inquires about possible market for his MSS; at work on a novel.

975   Typescript letter to Morty (Goldman), n.d. One page, with two holograph lines in pencil; typed signature. Another story ready for the *Post;* "I'll leave this to your judgment."

976   Typescript letter to Morty (Goldman), n.d. One page, signed "Faulkner." Sending "Bear Hunt" to the *Post.*

977   Typescript letter to Morty (Goldman), n.d. One page. Asks for return of story "This Kind of Courage," now being turned into a novel.

978   Typescript letter to Morty (Goldman), n.d. One page, signed "Faulkner." Is sending one story for the *Cosmopolitan.*

979   Typescript letter to Morty (Goldman), July 24, no year. One page, signed "Bill F." About recently completed "An Odor of Verbena" and its sale to the *Post.*

980   Holograph letter, no salutation, n.d. One page, seven lines, signed "F." About "Lo!" and another story for the *Post* or *Cosmopolitan.*

981   Typescript letter to Morty (Goldman), January 21, 1937. One page, signed "Bill." About contract for new book.

Reproduction of a typescript letter to Maurice Coindreau, February 26, 1937, Beverly Hills. One page, signed "William Faulkner." See 2769 Meriwether, "Check List." About proposed translation into French of *The Sound and the Fury.*

982   Typescript letter to Morty (Goldman), n.d. One page signed "Faulkner." Another story being sent for (Alfred) Dashiell at Scribner's.

983   Typescript letter to Morty (Goldman), February 19, 1938. Two pages with three holograph lines in ink, signed "Bill." Concerns Goldman's commissions.

984   Typescript letter to Morty (Goldman), n.d. One page, typed signature. Discusses "Fool about a Horse" and "The Brooch."

985   Typescript letter to Morty (Goldman), n.d. One page, typed signature "Bill F." Plans series of Reconstruction period stories.

986   Typescript letter to Morty (Goldman), n.d. One page, no signature. About negotiations with the *Post* for stories.

987   Beck, Warren. "Faulkner: A Preface and a Letter," *Yale Review*, LII, No. 1 (October 1962). Prints portion of a letter dated July 6, 1941, written by Faulkner to Beck.

Letter to Whit Burnett, July 1942, Oxford. One page, signed "Faulkner." See 692 Burnett, *America's 93 Greatest . . . ,* 1942.

988   Copy of a typescript letter to (Dayton) Kohler, January 10, 1950. One page, signed "William Faulkner." About Kohler's article in *College English.*

989 Letter to Richard Walser (n.d. n.p.). *The Enigma of Thomas Wolfe*, ed. Richard Walser. Cambridge: Harvard University Press, 1953. The "Asheville Edition," limited to 301 copies signed by Richard Walser. Copy No. 254. Faulkner on Wolfe.

990 Thermofax copy of a typescript letter to Dr. Bixler of Colby College, March 7, 1956. One page, signed "William Faulkner." Declines to accept honorary degree. Original at Colby College.

991 Holograph letter to Atcheson Hench (February) 20 (1957, Charlottesville). One page, signed "William Faulkner." Regrets inability to accept dinner invitation.

992 Letter to a student, "Mr. Kirk," March 8, 1956. *Crimson-White* (University of Alabama), LXII, No. 27 (June 9, 1963).

OTHER PRINTINGS

993 "Faulkner's Wisdom," *National Observer*, June 17, 1963.

994 Holograph letter to Edward McAleer, March 25, 1958, Oxford. One page, signed "William Faulkner." Conveys thanks for extension of privileges of the Colonnade Club, University of Virginia.

995 Typescript letter to John Cook Wyllie, "Monday, 6th" (May 1958). One page, signed "William Faulkner." With covering envelope. Accepts appointment as library consultant in American Literature at the Alderman Library, University of Virginia.

996 Typescript letter to John Cook Wyllie, September 10, 1958. One page, signed "William Faulkner." Accepts assignment of study room in Alderman Library, the University of Virginia.

997 Typescript letter to John Cook Wyllie, May 1959. One page, signed "William Faulkner." Authorizes transfer of all MSS, typescripts, and other material to the Alderman Library.

998 Two holograph lines signed "William Faulkner #8." On, and in reply to, a typescript letter addressed to all study room holders in Alderman Library, University of Virginia, and dated May 12, 1959. Faulkner states that room will not be needed during summer and fall.

999 Typescript letter to Linton Massey, "Oxford, Miss., Friday" (July 3, 1959). One page, signed "William Faulkner." Directs removal of certain MS pages.

1000 Typescript letter to Curator of Manuscripts, Alderman Library, University of Virginia, November 24, 1959. One page, signed "William Faulkner." Authorizes restoration of "A Rose for Emily" and other MSS.

1001 Typescript letter to Curator of Manuscripts, man Library, December 18, 1959. One page, signed Alderman Library, December 18, 1959. One page, signed "William Faulkner," with two autograph lines added. Authorizes withdrawal of "The Wishing Tree."

1002 Typescript letter to Weldon Cooper, October 10, 1960. One page, signed "William Faulkner," with envelope addressed in the author's handwriting. Acknowledges his appointment as Balch Lecturer in American Literature in the University of Virginia.

1003 Typescript letter to "Mr Wylie" (John Cook Wyllie), January 1, 1961. One page, signed "William Faulkner," with a three-word revision in the author's handwriting and with original envelope addressed in the author's handwriting. Concerns candidate for the scholarship grant by the William Faulkner Foundation at the University of Virginia.

1004 Three holograph lines signed "William Faulkner." On, and in reply to, a typescript letter to Faulkner from Fredson Bowers dated September 29, 1961. Approves entry in *University of Virginia Record*.

1005 Two holograph lines signed "William Faulkner." On, and in reply to, a typescript letter from Fredson Bowers dated December 9, 1961, and inviting him to attend an English Club party. Regrets.

THERE has been no bona fide collection in English of Faulkner's works. The present category comprises such collected editions as have not been fitted in elsewhere. Items are listed according to language—French, Italian, Spanish, and Japanese.

French

1006 *Jefferson, Mississippi*
Ed. with introduction by Michel Mohrt.
Paris: Club du Meilleur Livre, 1956.
Number 726 of 5500.
Contains the following short stories: "All the Dead Pilots," trans. R-N. Raimbault and H. Delgove; "The Bear," trans. R.-N. Raimbault; "Dry September," trans. M.-E. Coindreau; "A Justice," trans. R.-N. Raimbault and C.-P. Vorce; "A Rose for Emily," trans. M.-E. Coindreau; "That Evening Sun," trans. M.-E. Coindreau; "There Was a Queen," trans. R.-N. Raimbault and C.-P. Vorce; and "Wash," trans. R.-N. Raimbault and C.-P. Vorce.
Contains excerpts from the following works: *Absalom, Absalom!*, trans. R.-N. Raimbault; *Requiem for a Nun*, trans. M.-E. Coindreau; *Sartoris*, trans. R.-N. Raimbault and H. Delgove; *The Sound and the Fury*, trans. M.-E. Coindreau; and *The Unvanquished*, trans. R. N. Raimbault and C.-P. Vorce.
Also contains the "Appendix" to the Viking *Portable Faulkner*.

Italian

1007 *Tutte le opere di William Faulkner*
Ed. Fernanda Pivano.
Vol. II. *I Negri / e gli Indiani.* Milan: Mondadori, 1961.
Contains: *Go Down, Moses*, trans. Edoardo Bizzarri; *Intruder in the Dust*, trans. Fernanda Pivano; "Red Leaves," trans. Fernanda Pivano; "A Justice," trans. Fernanda Pivano; "Lo," trans. Magda De Cristofaro Mal-

dini; "A Courtship," trans. Magda De Cristofaro Maldini; and "Race at Morning," trans. Giorgio Monicelli.
Vol. III–IV. *I piantatori e i poveri bianchi / Le donne del Sud.* Milan: Mondadori, 1961.
Contains: *Absalom, Absalom!*, trans. Glauco Cambon; "Wash," trans. Fernanda Pivano; "Mountain Victory," trans. Giorgio Monicelli; *The Unvanquished*, trans. Alberto Marmont; "My Grandmother Millard," trans. Giorgio Monicelli; "All the Dead Pilots," trans. Giorgio Monicelli; "Ad Astra," trans. Fernanda Pivano; and "There Was a Queen," trans. Giorgio Monicelli.
Vol. VI. *La famiglia Stevens.* Milan: Mondadori, 1963.
Contains: *Sanctuary*, trans. Giorgio Monicelli; *Requiem for a Nun*, trans. Fernanda Pivano; and *Knight's Gambit*, trans. Elena Vivante.

Spanish

1008 *Obras completas*
Vol. I. Barcelona: Caralt, [1959]. "Primera edición." Preface by Mariano Orta. Contains: *Soldiers' Pay*, trans. not given, with illustrations by José M.ª de Martín; *Mosquitoes*, trans. Domingo Manfredi, with illustrations by Ismael Balanyá; *The Hamlet*, trans. J. Napoletano Torre and P. Carbó Amiguet, with illustration by Riera Rojas; and *Go Down, Moses*, trans. Ana María de Foronda, with illustrations by Hernández Pijoan.
Vol. II. Barcelona: Caralt, [1962]. "Primera edición." Contains: *Pylon*, trans. Julio Fernández-Yáñez, with illustrations by Álvero Delgado; *The Unvanquished*, trans. Alberto Vilá de Avilés, with illustrations by Pla Narbona; *As I Lay Dying*, trans. Arturo del Hoyo and Agustín Caballero, with illustrations by Luis Álvarez; and *A Fable*, trans. Antonio Ribera, with foreword by Agustín Bartra and illustrations by Francisco Echauz.

1009 *Obras escogidas*
Vol. I. Madrid: Aguilar, 1956. "tercera edición." Same translations as in *Obras completas*.
Contains: *As I Lay Dying, Pylon, The Unvan-*

quished, *The Hamlet*, and *Go Down, Moses*.

Vol. II.   Madrid: Aguilar, 1962.   "secunda edición."
Trans. Amando Lazaro Ros.

Contains: *A Fable, The Sound and the Fury, Sanctuary, Absalom, Absalom!*, "Barn Burning," "Shingles for the Lord," "The Tall Men," "Two Soldiers," "A Rose for Emily," "All the Dead Pilots," "Doctor Martino," "Pennsylvania Station," and "Artist at Home."

Japanese

1010   *Hibiki to ikari*

Tokyo: Mikasa Shobō, 1957. Trans. Masaō Takahashi.

Contains *The Sound and the Fury*, "Red Leaves," "Ambuscade," "Wash," "That Evening Sun," and "A Rose for Emily."

1011   *Gendai Amerika bungaku zenshu*

Tokyo, Arechi Shuppansha, 1958.   (Collection of Contemporary American Literature, Vol. VIII.) Trans. Junzaburo Nishiwaki *et al*.   Four copies.

Contains *Absalom, Absalom!*, "The Bear," "A Rose for Emily," and "That Evening Sun."

1012   *Shino tokoni yo kotawannte*

Tokyo: Takama Shobō, 1959.   (Collection of Modern Western Literature, Vol. LXI.)   Trans. Masami Nishikawa.

Contains *As I Lay Dying, Pylon*, "Mississippi," and Hemingway's *Farewell to Arms*.

THIS material is arranged chronologically.

1013 *Faulkner Reads from His Works.* 33⅓ r.p.m. phonodisc. Caedmon, TC 1035. 1954. Contains the Nobel Prize address and selections from *As I Lay Dying, A Fable,* and *The* [sic] *Old Man.*

1014 *Impressions of Japan.* 16 mm. sound film. [1955?]

1015 *William Faulkner Reads from His Works.* 33⅓ r.p.m. phonodisc. M-G-M, E 3617 ARC. 1957. Contains selections from *The Sound and the Fury* and *Light in August.*

1016 "Faulkner in the University." Compiled by Frederick L. Gwynn and Joseph L. Blotner. Forty-one tape recordings. 1957–1958. Recordings of Faulkner's lectures and classroom conferences in and around Charlottesville; the basis of *Faulkner in the University.*

1017 *Faulkner at Virginia.* 16 mm. sound film in color. 1960. Produced by the University of Virginia School of General Studies; directed by James S. Helms. Audio from the Gwynn and Blotner tape recordings of Faulkner; video from still photographs.

1018 "That Evening Sun." Tape recording made by Faulkner for Recording for the Blind, Inc. May 23, 1960.

There is also a recording of Faulkner reading Irwin Russell's poem "Christmas Night in the Quarters," as broadcast over Radio Station WELK, Charlottesville, Va., December 14, 1961.

ITEMS in this section are arranged by date.

1019 Drawings. *Ole Miss: The Year Book of the University of Mississippi*, Vol. XXII (1917–1918). Two signed drawings. Two copies.

1020 ——. Vol. XXIV (1919–1920). Four signed drawings, one unsigned, p. 29. Also includes references to Faulkner; two photographs. Includes poem, "To a Co-ed."

1021 Cartoon. *Ole Miss: The Year Book of the University of Mississippi*, Vol. XXVI (1922). Unsigned cartoon, p. 188; also numerous references to Faulkner. Unsigned drawings, in William Faulkner's style, may be the work of his brother, John, whose style was similar. Any definite attribution without specific evidence would be wholly gratuitous.

1022 Drawing. *The Scream*, I, No. 5 (May 1925), 13–14, 19–20. Presumably a proof sheet.

1023 The "Beer" broadside (1950). One sheet, printed on recto only. 28 x 21 cm. Copy 1. Copy 2: Has holograph notes by Professor Harold G. Brown of the English Department of the University of Mississippi. See Plate XIV.

1024 "Notice." Oxford (Miss.) *Eagle*, October 15, 22, 29, 1959. Photostat of advertisement posting Faulkner's woods. See Plate XV.

TO THE VOTERS OF OXFORD

Correction to paid printed statement of Private Citizens H. E. Finger, Jr., John K. Johnson, and Frank Moody Purser.

1. *'Beer was voted out in 1944 because of its obnoxiousness.'*

   Beer was voted out in 1944 because too many voters who drank beer or didn't object to other people drinking it, were absent in Europe and Asia defending Oxford where voters who preferred home to war could vote on beer in 1944.

2. *'A bottle of 4 percent beer contains twice as much alcohol as a jigger of whiskey.'*

   A 12 ounce bottle of four percent beer contains forty-eight one hundreths of one ounce of alcohol. A jigger holds one and one-half ounces (see Dictionary). Whiskey ranges from 30 to 45 percent alcohol. A jigger of 30 percent whiskey contains forty-five one hundreths of one ounce of alcohol. A bottle of 4 percent beer doesn't contain twice as much alcohol as a jigger of whiskey. Unless the whiskey is less than 32 percent alcohol, the bottle of beer doesn't even contain as much.

3. *'Money spent for beer should be spent for food, clothing and other essential consumer goods.'*

   By this precedent, we will have to hold another election to vote on whether or not the florists, the picture shows, the radio shops and the pleasure car dealers will be permitted in Oxford.

4. *'Starkville and Water Valley voted beer out; why not Oxford?'*

   Since Starkville is the home of Mississippi State, and Mississippi State beat the University of Mississippi at football, maybe Oxford, which is the home of the University of Mississippi, is right in taking Starkville for a model. But why must we imitate Water Valley? Our high school team beat theirs, didn't it?

   Yours for a freer Oxford, where publicans can be law abiding publicans six days a week, and Ministers of God can be Ministers of God all seven days in the week, as the Founder of their Ministry commanded them to when He ordered them to keep out of temporal politics in His own words: 'Render unto Caesar the things that are Caesar's and to God the things that are God's.'

William Faulkner
Private Citizen

XIV. The "Beer" broadside

ty and Mississippi will
danger.
urce of cash to Lafay-
ire of the majority of
's people are express-
passing of laws govern-
the people. Those who
these laws are there-
g against the b_st in-
the people with whom
. The hunter who
sly drops a match,
forest fir..on land he
own is violating the
liable for his actions.
r who burns his fields
it get into someone
had broken the law.
ississippi forest fire
s follows:
Woods Firing is a
B.N. 120. Section 1,
22 Laws of 1954: "If
wilfully, malicious-
onlously sets on fire
, meadow, field or
t his own, he shall
of a felony and shall,
ction be sentenced to
penitentiary for not
two years, not less
year, or fined not
two hundred dollars
than one year, or
ss than two hundred
more than one
dollars or both in the
of the court.
Fire To Escape To
Another is a Mis-
H. D. No. 120 Section
222, Laws of 1954
ty person negligently
only causes fire to be
ted to any woods,
ursh, field or prairie
., he shall be guilty
canor, and shall, on
be fined not less
ty dollars nor more
hundred dollars, or
in the county jail
an three months, or
e discretion of the

suppressing fire may
ed by recognized
person or firm re-
aws, 1940, Chapter
UPPRESSION, Fires
nuisance-abatement

sance by reason of its menac-
to life and property.
Any person, firm or corpor.-
tion negligently or wilfully a: .
maliciously responsible for th
starting or the existence of suc
fire on land other than his ov
hereby required to control
copration shall wilfully refus-
neglect or fail to do so, any o
ganized fire suppression agenc
recognized by the Mississip
Forestry Commission, may sun
marily abate the nuisance th..
constituted by controlling or ex
inguishing the fire.
The costs of abating such
nuisance by civil action in the
proper court. Action for said re-
covery to be filed by the agency
abating the nuisance. Provided
that this act shall not impair
any remedy now allowed by
law.

While most men swear by
wood as a throughly masculine
material, the ladies are also get-
ting in their say. Wood paneled
walls are frequent fixtures in
the feminine domains, such as
bedrooms, parlour, bath and
kitchen. Modern finishes pro-
vide a delicate coloring of m
lady's choice, while the natural
masculinity of the material is
further subdued by the refined
satin-smooth look of the clear
grades of lumber.

Curved ceiling beams of lami-
nated lumber, slanting upward
at their outer extremities, are
giving a distinctly Oriental cast
to contemporary homes of plank-
and-beam construction.
The natural gold and tannish
tints of Southern Pine make it
easy to achieve a biege effect
with this type of wood panel
ing. Biege is one of the most
popular hues for modern dec-
oration.

Traffic in Karachi, capital of
Pakistan, is complicated by a
wide variety of conveyances.
There are 15 types of registered
transport, ranging from new
American automobile to pedicabs
and camel carts.

"NOTICE"

The posted woods on my property inside the city limits
of Oxford contain several tame squirrels. Any hunter who
feels himself too lacking in woodcraft and marksmanship
to approach a dangerous wild squirrel, might feel safe with
these. These woods are a part of the pasture used by my
horses and milk cow; also, the late arrival will find them
already full of other hunters   He is kindly requested not
to shoot either of these.

William Faulkner

This is
featherbedding

XV. Photostat of a page of the Oxford (Miss.) *Eagle* showing a notice posting Faulkner's woods

XII TYPESCRIPTS AND HOLOGRAPH MATERIAL NOT OTHERWISE CATALOGUED

THE material in this section is arranged chronologically.

1025 Typescript (September 1924). One page. Autobiographical sketch by William Faulkner.

1026 Holograph note, December 27, 1960. One page; nine lines in Faulkner's handwriting on verso. Other titles on verso and recto in another hand. Gives partial list of books wanted for the library at "Knole" in Albemarle County, Virginia, for possible later use by his grandchildren. For reproduction of verso, see 1147 Blotner, Joseph L., *William Faulkner's Library*, 1964.

1027 Receipt, dated February 13, 1960. One page, in Faulkner's handwriting and signed "William Faulkner." For oil painting of the author by his mother, following the close of the Faulkner Exhibition, "Man Working, 1919–1959," at the University of Virginia.